After rolling **doughnuts** in grounds to be playing.

story is on childhood starting on themselves.

Life and life's aim knowing and that are in mind emotion gowning,

1. wake up your mind.

On the middle size green hill, West on the slice steep hill seen on ground with basic white color`s cows seed and the seed with yellow brown lightly them seeding peacefully on the light steep hill on the ground is slice yellow green head rise to the sky from the sky come on the light with weight winds coming and booming.

Is seed the over hill the cows seed that deep brown of seed to eating shapely as mouth that into the teeth to cross seeds of breath and next on one Is the noising breaths to blooms water bell boom. Other is the into noise rising moistening steam sometimes singing sounds.

the on the ground flicking seeds by

slighting winding handing toward to the green sky and from angled on the down ground with smelling moister freshly of winds blooming come to the cows' Groupe side long leg to yellow brown dark toile is smell feeling. between the leg side seen far away up and down into under steep lack stones flooding the long narrow water into by slice falling moister toiles,

on the small hill under flowing green and white's clouds on sky with the brown seemly green birds go on by middle size lack stone is strolling broken thin lack by winds,

often listen the sound of seeds by

cross as lightning winds. `Mom' I am going there now!

Around white cloud side flowing winds 's feeling like dem cooling is listening and going down to the under hill the mountains have cute face in white. blue, brown eye.

`Mom' I am incredibly happy because I am very Have morning time!

I am do not know me. But I know my Life in morning feeling freshly that I am go out now. Listening bright yellow seed then often walked the girl's blue shoes.

With moister, going down quietly.

Go to the under hills, she sees the

narrow waterline following currenting one`s seed, which brighten yellow.

brown color light. That head is little twisted and wetted. Is Side each other different small stone one has been moister ugly small stone, other is lighting brown color is dry. The other is narrow waterline following currency. Seen over bright white snow mountains of top such as the cocoa spread whited bread as seen.

Little steeped that cows seen one of two is seeding one is small and have little black bule color pack the other is large cow than on the head,

one more time cycling dame winds to

me, surface doing rounding in hole in waterline is appearing or disappearing and one more appearing. Slice currenting waterline flowering going. At side small flower leap grown,

that side is that seeing to the white and blue light color's sky going on growling. Moister had green leaf on small groups sleeping and go down that basic deep brown on yellow color's group fly up and down on left or right. After twenty. she is going down and have reached. Seen her mother make morning juice.

mom! I am going out and on in now.

Her mother smile to the me.

In her room is have bathroom with two grades highly.

In left is small table and in right is wardrobe. In room little moister air currency on in. in on ground make by dry and make wood brightly.

by windows little sunlight in going on to in, the warm be feeling has been in mind.

Nancy! where you are?

mom! `I am here'! `I am going now!' to her have answer. ` Have breakfast '! She going to kitchen hurry.

In the kitchen is that small made be dry wood and chair is having be painting as white ark color each other.

Mom today is I would have cooked breakfast food is what is?

Perhaps... orange juice and half one bread...! now have delicious. On the plate is little brown yellow and that little side is reflecting lighting little red, yellow colors. Mom! thank you.

Go on eat, and mom gives me white milk. so do I know mom! Mom smile to me. Surround is window over come in bright yellow light by eye righting is quietly. Listening. Bird's sings, that my favorite song such as, I am glace.

After I am meal, I am going to near my house on back yard.

There are lot of kinds of green woods

and flowers with white yellow, red. and bugs with each other forms, vegetables such as corns and carrot, onion on. There is small playground that go to. Dark-brown color's toil is a footing mark by my walking, the playground is each on surface is a slice ugly hold seeing and each other normally flatted.

There is I am feeling freely and beautifully and

Freshly, healthy, and mom' natural gently that to me have that love feeling have me that cause Foot by me under toils seen little wet has mixed the of air and morning moisture and plants and around in flower 'scent and plants leafed that feeling.

she is too has fined out flowers, the flowers are green and she' eye blighted by to red, yellow light reflected. the flower is tulips. the Next is twisting by sometime come here wind on blue sky seeing for me.

 At small ground I breathe to listens through air to flowers by vegetables by doing sound's singing songs, on ground green seeds each other, Moving up and down be dancing. Following on the Yellow green cons' steam that slice dark white color's brush moved up and down by fresh air in.

she is walking to the other.

There and stop. Ugly small pets are going on the that is be there. Be only they favorite secrete; she sees under into the ground play only themselves world in original life. Born and dye, Hunt, Love, Happy. Please go on however they always the same and cycling, she is seeing the pets and to the sky rising head with dark-brown colors after long moment. Once more walking them went to. She wears simple pants that is having made by her mother from long ago. I have on a something. Because my love mother made that. She ongoing stopped by moment .and Head go to the sky. The sky is bule with wet air in moister.

Go down perhaps the pet is going on to its life aim once more head do rise to the sky.

She reviews around and around with Hand stirring in the seeds. Suddenly in seeds groups small forge get into the left yard and a walk get to the moment. I am feeling myself in mean is surround plants, narrow waterline, pets, cows, winds about go on that gentle.

at long away slice steep likely I see to me run a deer with yellow brown in deep brown 's potted to small cycles, it is in noes downs it on and into the ground.

moment by moment current, with moister mixes breathy, have been seeing around.

suddenly. Into the down is brighten by in cloud by blocked sun slightly go out shoes' head surface is being wrinkly; I like my shoes is mom give me it made to by fabric and thin leader.

time to time I see down, likely my mine is fly, that' please, the surround is comfortable. my mine in grimly and with slice walking.

After by slow walking then sees back, at a little long distance my in made wood house seen comfortable and peacefully there, cow is quietly seeding. I am going up the narrow foot load with moister .my mouth's being breathing.

Side is about largely and with being brown and yellow, I surround in filed seeing that are cover with flowers on ground by, as my hand cuts one steam of seeds. And the little get in my mouth and as teeth up and down have biting the taste is please and sweetly.

now mixed cold and worm winds windy to the seed 'head with ahead and after, up and down, Shaked by winds. She more and little more going in the paly ground enters to the center.

After getting times current, she one more sees backyard' to the house. she' is in mind her.

Mother always love to be thankful. My mother is my very favorite mother. My mother is having me be born and to now and be care of me hardly, in hand made clothes and shoes. In back yard harvest in gowning corns, and carrots and apples.

Little grown that slice green, red color's strawberry and blueberry and go on and onions. Ahead going a walk there are low cons that is light green colors with small seeds rise dark-brown toile over there winds once more.

My hairs wave by sometime winds comes. that one strand is on my face by windy.

I walk following a narrow road with wet rode. Head turn to the sky in slice white and blue color with campers is, I like my mom near to me do not speaking. I old seven. But myself on the work. Seeing over there, there small house or that made of wood house with white colors. Is back yard and seen dogs that front is white basic small and medium black, blue spot basic withed surface that near small that' Is that doing bark going on to anything aim coming over to on oneself.

The two is simple playing. each other barks and bite, lamb, and after moment naturally be sleeping,

one more time I see the sky with slice black, white clouds. Next house living in, grandfather. grandchildren. father elder brother, elder sister. and my friend is Judy, he often there goes play to comfortable with natural, my friend is hansom and innocence and pretty, something has a sometime time, calling him. He and I must be playing with together.

2. under wood shades to yourself.

I like reading books, and I always be sitting the front of desk. To reading book's kinds are historical, language, mathematics, fiction, and nonfiction, go on.

the upstairs is that the most made wood that cozy, upstairs is windows have two' store. One is one stored room, the other is lightly windy booms in out windows, feeling is cleaning and refreshing in my mind and now. On morning birds come here on wood side windows sing song, that sounding I am two stored room. please, the birds have small and on basic slice brown is in black spot, that birds always smile to me such as friend to me come on.

May up stair be pleased to only me the room. My there often reading and sleeping and spent, from one hour to three hours but I am Stay all day in upstairs.

At morning can see the rising sun, afternoon worm sun, evening sunset of red color 's beautiful sun. I down stair with basic brown, yellow is lighting. `

Mom' I am hungry

Her mother is not kitchen.

She researches everywhere but is not.

Mom! After long. mom come here. Mon.

where you are?

I was back yard to reserve cooking got to vegetables being Cooke, mom! her' cycling face is bright lighting.

`Let go in kitchen"!

In her hand was lifting vegetable.

I am sitting front of meal desk. Mom' cooking time take long,'and I am going out. To take care of tire times, moment on going out.

My mom tells me to ` little spend time pass and go in!

My mom is cooking, and I am playing with painting on toile ground on backyard. Flying sometime on the sky to plane.

In backyard is corns it I eat as long as mom calling to me. I run to my house.

Mom! I am here now.

Have meal? Yes! I am answer and go in bedroom and wash hand with water. and I out, go on and sit-down chair making of yellow colors' wood chair.

`Have meal, my love cute!

On desk is on before getting it from backyard clean vegetable and, breads and juices that she got pay on town.

On After Little time they have each other quietly.

Little after She tells me,

`Nancy!' it once, could have eat. perhaps 'it be made of vegetable and vinegar have mixed.'

I eat with bread, which get into my mouth, I was feeling fresh,

My in mouth near fully to delicious foods. And little moment

I drink juice little and little.

` Mom'! I have well eaten meal. I must go upstairs to having study.

Let be there.

After moment I rise the chairs and go into the made of wood stairs. slowly gone up that.

My second secreted room is books be back and two story's bed, the on bed is cute pig doll, sometimes I talk with dolls. The dolls give me playing and, it be friend, be mom, be elder brother, be sisters, be fathers, be teacher, be cookers, Be ...

Hi cute dolls, I love. I am now study it everybody like that, but everybody does not like that. I am like it. Specially I am like

`Historical.' Do you like study or not?

Well. Do you like we will study... do not you!?

If you like that you will have to reading book to basic start. However, you would have been not study. Doll has answer.

I like start book before reading and I now can read the highly level to my ability. Well. I have answer.

`What's kind do you want reading book?'
I question to doll.

At moment before she tells me, after has answer.

I have to mathematics. the doll had been full pride of her face,

`Are you want one more book?' so I do full smile now and, so moment after, she wants to storybook with us in make emotion. I have found the book and hand on her. she has thankful to me. Through windows the windy come in and out that Sicily. Over there seen Sicily moving leap with windy. Feeling Little chilly. After two hours, I go down.

Now mom is busily cleaning Livingroom.

Mom is always busy.

I go out to yard, there playing with examination plants forms.

One is ugly forms, other is cycling and the form is variety. Cons's steam was growing, from three day to five-day sprout and that grown is from two month to three month. I talking to plants. the plants Smalling to me. just moment one more have seen... almost grown corns are steam is upright to up and down. Cons with Coverup by leap there get out form by seen my eyes. perhaps walk to take one hours to on narrow load long distance from my house there is small area in water currency. on where summer swimming and on winter riding skate and on spring and autumn is rest aera. Now I rest in mine to there is a plants, birds, insect, and flower especially rose, so on...

Over there to the windy blooms crossed mixed in and to water steam rise surface on the puddle is beautiful. I see feeling flower leap is white, yellow. Red brown color is combinate each other now the small is much comfortable. I take out socks and go in medium size cycling puddle. it is cool... moment. I am going out. Yet, I was feeling slice chilly.

Surround seeing tour end, I am going to my house. on front is immature seeds, I go in to fast walk the inside groups.

Sometimes I am feeling to stick by seeds. Here and there stir lightly by both hands. I am going on to me seen small bird cage, and I come to return that, near have an exam my house with white color made of wood. One more time seeing clean and blue green sky. `Mom! Over there?``` I come in!' I get in house.

The then my mom had cooking. I wash hand and hire and foot, get in my bedroom. Have been sleeping. Around for thirty minutes.

3. Have a suitable time with my friends!

I walk up before two minutes being afternoon. My mom is in kitchen and made meal. At morning eat that have differently, Nancy! `Have meal!' yes mom! I go on now! I am talking to my mom about to me to gone out playing that. mom is small to me, mom' herself is thinking about my daughter is oneself doing working because, I have meal the bread pick in cheese. And juice. on afternoon meal is pulsed carrot. That have boiling and bob take on that is eating, the teats is sweet and delicious,
After eating I go out to play with next

house' friend. his name is John, he is man, we are play to doctor play and father and Mother play and playing game it is very joining than we meet. always each other have please speaking. `Are you lunch?'

Yes! And you? Yes, I am.

Hello! `Nancy 'how do you do? Jon is question after moment,

Nice meet you! Nancy responds about the question.

Are we play? Of course! what of play game? Jon is question.

Have we It talking about noun? Nancy responsible.

Ok! ` how do your way,' it is easy. If I imagination the one noun. You are question to me to imagination noun, example, me thinking cows. Then you question to my thinking that imagination about you do not know noun, ok?

Yes! Jon is responsible to that. Now. Starte! Nancy is thinking to the boll. Jon have question large and small? Nancy responsible, it weathers big or small! Is color whether dark or bright? Nancy has responsible about questions. it is brightly but the brightest. Nancy has responsible. Eat or do not eat?

`Do not eat'! Nancy responsible.

Then working usage that. or playing usage that. Jon has questions. then doing play usage that. Ok! Jon is little known the noun, usage of what of body is that... hand or foot?

Foot usage and hand usage. Nancy answer about Jon' questions. It is boll. It is, ok? Jon's face is more blighting with surely, Nancy is smalling to him, and tell, him, that is right!

Each other face full as please.

Both each other themselves gone to house.

Little been dry on ground than before pass little time.

In house mom reading book, I am quietly in my room. In room on moment after, I am going in the bathroom, and wash hand foot, and hair, do it after, I am going in kitchen, have drink milk.

My mom is reading books, I am going upstairs to study middle on stair of going surround is clean and yellow colors is whyever I am feeling is fulling stomach to mom` love. At upstairs study is please and I do have mathematics study hard. In math is very variety contents that is have to me that be known, do not have known that. Example, land long,

Fruit count, mom! 'Height long,' take time to go, have to make that size go on, after pass three hours I go kitchen and give to mom thankful' manner, one more time pass to me I am going.

Bedroom to sleeping. And naturally

sleeping. After one hour, I wake up sleeping, having yawn and take on shoes and go directly the in bathroom I am wash face. and hand. One more going up stairs, my two floor is cleanly and quiet. I sit on the

Chaired and was study. After One hour my mom call me that come on now in the kitchen. I responsible `yes! I as much as hear sound' that mom call to me rightly go in the kitchen there are a variety cooked food. That is bob, kimchi, bread. Jam, butter. Kim bob, juice, noodle. so on. I have delicious the food after, and I have been drinking juice. Mom! thankful but could you allow me to go out? Mom is responsible to my question. `yes'! but before darked, you must return in house. I go out and out was little chilly. surrounded is dark blue sky by sunset. Plants and pets are quiet. Sometime the light bug sound listens to me, I am walking round my house be little distance. Air is fresh. The fresh air gives to me comfortable and peace, happy, passing thirty minutes, my foot be to in my house, mom! Nancy is calling.

Why? Nancy? Mom is speaking.

Mom! I am going in,

Yes! Mom answer...

I one more reading book about mathematics

After and speaking with doll. How old are you? I am two old.

Because I buy that before one year, and two old...

But what is your name? I do not know because I do not have make my name. could you make your name? and tell you?

` Yes'! thank you! Doll was answer.

After moment I think to make name, how do you call pig?

Pig is pig how about?

The d being go in coffee,

Thank you come in; May I help you? Pig talks to me.

Is your resister order? Pig seeing now with smiling. Well, you are name is pig. could you, ok? Pig? Pig have answer that is all right!

My in brain on occasionally calling that pig, pig, pig.

Hi pig. what would you like during middle dinner time?

I like to have to the coffee service playing, man is pig and passenger is mine. Ok? Yes. Passenger

have talk to me.

Yes! I like coffee, please!

What would you like kind of coffee?

I want black coffee please!

What kind do you like choice of black coffee, slice or medium or deep?

I like medium, please!

Just moment, could you have to wait for fifty minutes, please!

Yes! Thank you.! I am talk to that.

After moment, I am calling the pig. Hi host. Could you get me newspaper? Yes! But I don' t understands, any newspaper or not. There are content kinds of newspaper, example economic. Currency. Political, weekly. Dally. Monthly go on... would you like choice? Pig is talk that.

Yes, I like economic dally. I talk to that.

After moment, yes! here are!

Thank you. I am reading newspaper and pig is come to me coffee get it with sugar. thank you, sir.

Of reading Newspaper I often little

drinking black coffee. After Newspaper reading completed, I see time .and wait the train arrives at ten twenty. Dir pig sent talk about another service request. Can I help you.! Oh no problem. Could you send me napkins? Me question.

Yes, I take it to you.

Thank you.!

After moments, pig get it to me.

In the room worm and silent often hear of inset sound

Nancy! do You go in?

Yes! Mom! Come here...!

Yes...!

I am going have downstairs, go to the kitchen. moms give me apple of fruits.

then my apple bite in mouth go in, I am listening that tooth moving to up and down in the mouth.

After have refreshment, I talk with mom about that sleeping reserve. Today night is slicing the chillier than yesterday. I go my bedroom to sleeping, good night mom, doll's pig sir!

h

4. often rest under the cloud shadows in daily life.

In morning yellow bright light shine me, that wake me from my dream, but another that Waite be me to one more start newly. as the normal time, I early get up in the morning, of bathroom in house is wash face and teeth. And dried my face by scope and go out to the back yard there I have brash, movement, as what then, I am walk cross narrow road, as time as fresh air and natural beautiful be feeling to me. I am understanding dally exchange environment to my surround. But, the change little by little must be complete, I am walking and seeing growing plant, vegetable. wood, I like myself. And

Hi! Jon. good morning! How do you do? Nice, enjoyable time,

We each other meet have to communication, and to playing.

Could you have diner? I am already bite; how do you do have playing? he tall to me.

Yes! What is play with me to healthy.

I like walking. now? I love everything, outline then go five minutes appear the natural garden ever do not seen scene. Surrounded variety kind wood is, and fountain of garden, on ground is the stone floor. In middle is flowers with variety colors with red, yellow. Blue. And variety kind plants are, rose, tulip, and lily, from garden's entrance starting to the end post is shape line form fencing with wood plants. I do not know about on here. And I am surprised the scene. We walk in the garden. On being derationed a stone, we once more have think funny playing that noun relay game is, floor.

Nancy is start! Jon is have talked. Well... EliZe's next, Jon?

Smite, next Nancy? Herro. Next Jon? Well. false ...! could you tell.

Me that? Yohan. ki ki.... One more time, Nancy? Jon is as powerful as spoken to me. We will let us start.!

Chocolate. Nancy is speaking. Elegance.!
Elite. Next Nancy? Jon is having speaking.
Eagle... Next Jon is speaking to me.!
Ellice.

Nancy spoken to him.! Earthe.

Have one more rest.! Nancy is do not
think about that noun... each other walks
sing song well.

Connection I and John little and little open
the mind' door to mi. Middle size fountain
of garden is.at big town I have seen that,
now here can see to me, is surprising.
Found is highly perhaps my west, I am
drunken into my mouth to head bends to
down. I am feeling very cooling and
cleaning. And I put water on my hand and

thrown to Jon. are you cool? Nancy is speaking. or Jon is so do... are you cool...? each other it is playing after, each other 's face was full the water drops, nanny and Jon walk side by side into the garden woods. One more time slice wind come on my face, and I once more was feeling cooling, sometime chilly wind is feeling. Before Jon is back home, he must tell you that next good spot teaches you, one hour later and or Nancy go back her house. From there to her house take two hours. My shoes are duty with water and toils is each other mixed. Mom! I am going in! `well'! I go in the bathroom to wash my shoes and my face. Foot. Hand, hair...

mom is cooking at kitchen. After I do wash, go to up stair, perhaps there.

Is comfortable. What is that kind of reading books today. Today is having to read books about our nation historical. In content is original start nation is Dangun is has be cocreate nation is that when Hwang and whenua original nation is having creation,

Had exchanged be Tongil Silla and that is Blaha exchanged.

After gore been, contents of historical books are reading, after,

Books folds and gone to the kitchen, mom I must lunch now! Mom is what is today menu go on smile to me smiling, to me question. I was thanking this or that in my head and talked to mom. that is bread.! Me told,

Have nice answer, and jam, and cheeses, mom is being smiling that have cooking stay on desk. What do you like have to playing? To me like playing is noun set on question be noun,

I told to my mom, far go on smiling.

I am going out the meal and go bathroom to teeth brushing. and I am going to change wear, walking into the bedroom, in the room exchange wear .and go out house, out is clean air is going in my breath noise, I am very happiness. I wake up.

Natural is a particularly important that. Today is `where are going'? I

Must going long distant, I must back home before noon,

Walke Narrow Road, side seed gowning fully, ground is ugly small stone stays were and there. Flat and strong road's surface is on the ground. The road is slightly up deep and slightly down deep, me go there is questions about what' form? Is environmental? is peculiarity? ...

Wind is bloom to me slice, to my side face, on the blue-sky birds fly freely and orderly. Sky is highly and green, slice to down pass two minutes on the road reached, there is small flower group that white and green, yellow color's is. The name is wild chrysanthemum. Seeing around head, as that is pine that kang-a-ji-fool, there and where on ground grown that jab Choo. Leaf is cycling forth direction divided that Toki-fool...

The Long distance from be there to current narrow waters to drink that animals come here near me. I am going up slice high narrow county road and or walked one hours and come here from my house take long, ongoing walk I am rest on the large flat rock for twenty minutes, seeing to sky is not change that white, blue color's form. After moment I going to the near narrow water to. There I ate water and washed face. I am feeling freshly on my sit, I am viewing surround woods, on the left is reflect sun' shine. that come in eye be to brightly. Other shine is on narrow water 'on wave that eyebright is reflect to me by shine, come in... on the narrow water is front of small wood is slice up and down moving, and the side small slice brown birds fly through on the narrow water from front and to back...

moment after.

Pass fifty minutes, I get up the on stay, I must go back, and I brush shoes after gone back to my house, I am going to road, up and down, and to road with be woods left, or right...

Over there my house seen to me, my face seen smile such much that have it. Such then I have... mom! At long distance to easily listen to sound as big talk I am to house that be to be certainly. My mind and I have been up to the to come through the think about peaceful, go in my house that my mom was resting to sit on the comfortable chair with listen to radio in her hand. Mom involved in radio. I quietly go in my bedroom .and sleeping for one hour. But did not is flash meal, sometime my mom wake to me be sleeping. I open eye, seen mom' comfortable face, I am once or once more being my right-hand slice cross on my eyes, at the bedroom, had go out, to wash to me. After I am question to my mom. What's Today breakfast? mom!

Today's breakfast is noodle! Mom was answer with smile.

How do make it? I have curiosity to questions to mom.

It made of bundle and source.

Are you ease? Mom! yes! can I have helped a way? Mom's face with full of smile more than...

Outside listening bird's busy crying sounds. May think or to have been black fast time?! At out Windows come in sun's light is brightly to shining in house's there and were. mom! teacher to me, please!

Mom is once more be smiling,

Nancy! noodle made methods is to in noodle dumping black source soya's. You get understanding it. Yes!

Have Nancy make noodle? yes. I must make it. Tell her, and on front of desk sitting waiting for material to noodle give to me from mom. Five minutes later, my mom stays on the table. On and I sitting to seeing the on-scene mom made do noodle cooking follows you made of noodles. To made ease to me...

Noodle Manu is today best black fast to me. on dinner, mom give me radio's song is on feeling as comfortable and please.

One plate is all things! mom speaks to me with please smiling.

Mom! unbelievably delicious! So talked and gone at in my bedroom.

To had Rest sleeping in room. after one hour, on own oneself get up on room. Over window's cut ten side, slice wind boom in my room. I am going out, and to go in my upstairs up wood made stairs, step by, to up. Then seen my friend is. Doll.pig.ki ki...

Hi pig? Nice meet you! me speaking to my friend.

Pig told me. How do we play game?

Have today is train playing? me tell pig.

I am passenger and, pig is train attendants

all right.

Ok!

Have train reaching at in the station is the passengers orderly is crowd, hello sir. Yes... each other bowing of crews and passengers. Get in the train after moment, crew attendant walking through the in-train passageway, excuse me? Can I author you are ticket? Pig is having request.

Of course, it mine. I am giving to ticket is that made of paper. my chair number is the left thirty-five of two train case, ok! What you are destination? pig is tell me.

My destination is Ulsan. Could you tell me why you go to there?

To I am playing there with my curson and

my country! Passenger speaking.

Pig sure my ticket and I receive that ticket.

Have nice journey. thank you. Pig to me bowing and go through train pass way, outside train is someone people setting up train, someone waiting for next train.

Train playing ending! Pig is speaking.

Aha very shot, it' not fun. I little false and over there seeing to mountain, I want to have gone there with covered snow then mountain. After moment I waked up by mom's calling to.

5 Hope to the one more time in mind.

I wake up by my mom's calling at three o'clock. I am reading to choose book is science books. The in science is we do not know things, and I once more have done review nouns in books, after study, I down in the living room that her mom is also reading books, go through hallway seen kitchen there I drank juice quietly. And once thinking then have lunch that noodle. And mom! could you allow go out now? Yes! you do.!

Thank you, mom! Then I go out. and I am going out into flash air. Backyard is to be cover with slice black clouds that leaf is seeing to black on green colors. On black on green colors back is cons is from slice divided tip be view yellow colors thanking to near grown that, wind is slice flow under my head. and moment worm air come on me, my mine hold to worm comfortable. Moment, in the sky down slice rain, I hurry up run in the house near storehouse, fortunately slice wet my wears. In storehouse is lot that, variety agricultural, watering sparkling can, manure, fertilizer. so, on... slice winds bloom to me lightly and after my moister be wet wear is on little more, that do been dried Mind is peaceful. I am in dark hole and go out into bright back yard, and breath freshly air into my minds, hello my natural! I am well. Are ok as I am happy.! in the sky shines lighting bright with white and harmony mixed reds and yellow and blue` colors. Back yard as such has a beautiful decoration scene. On the ground is mixed toil' duty and rain moister, shot long time, I walk on the narrow road. slice cool air is sometimes winding from side to head before. Surround I am. plant' s leaves move slice up and down and stir left and right in the air. I am going my house. mom! go in. I am telling my mom. Have do drink worm milk, is over there. thank you, mom! Mom is quietly siting sleeping. Before that have do not ever fleeing worms, I can feel worms in the house. I go in bathroom to wash and go in bedroom and have exchange wear and have sleeping in the bed.

Nancy! Have dinner! Mom is waked me at by. I am open quietly my eyes. White basic green form written dress have been wearing mom stand me by. Yes! Mom!

I am going out at bed, and pass living room go to kitchen, and

Sits front of dinner desk, `mom,' what's today dinner?

Today's dinner is cow soups.

Do not smell? I am concern that.

My mom gentle tall me. no! and have smile to me.

White and yellow's colors are combination that are high feeling delicious, and white painted on form on plate stays quietly bread' one cake picking in soup and have eat. Mom is seeing.

Comfortable front of me eating gently. and smile to me, mom?

Why? Could you give me juice? I do a little speaking to have that require to mom, which is all right, so do mom do be answers lowly tons, mom, and me, each other is smile. Well, have eat it, now. Mom! Could you give me once more soup?

Ok! Let Us It see. I have two plates, and after moment rest, I am going my bedroom to change wears.

My mother is always taking care of me. and I am always happy.

I am gone there. that I am brush my hair and wash face. Seen

Out of windows is in the dark that is being little shining to my house by start light. The next stars seen being the moon that is with white and yellow lighting color. darkly and chilly night with surrounding that be quietly. But in my room is to be warm and be coz. I am now sleeping, ` mom' good night it. As much, I had the listening sound far from will be mom' answer. I wake up by my mon. before I rise sun on the

ground, it is morning. I get up and I am

orderly the bed and go berth room and wash having hand up and down to face and get back my wear exchange and brush my bed and room. Directly go to the kitchen, there have eats meal. Today morning meal is rice. White rice was do see as very clearly. Side is.

kimchi. And I had bob, and kimchi. Was unbelievably delicious with me.

tongue and teeth mixed in my mouth with spicy and bitter.

smile. and after I drink milk. all the time.! I have meal with my mother. After mom has meal, seen to me with smiling, I am going up to upstairs be my room. Hi doll or pig sir.! I am please bow to my friend, so do dolls bow me with please. Hi pig would you like joining playing? Yes! what's? I like mathematics playing. how would you do play. Pig questions me. Perhaps

in alphabets as plus and miners do now, example, at one plus one is two, here on two, if you have count one more two

having you count have, the alphabet once more two as call, three plus calls, you must answer is five. Are you ok?

If Pig is understanding, head moved up and down, let us start!

One plus two! I am question.

Three! Pig is answer.

Plus, five. And miners four.! I am question.

Four! Pig is answer.

You are excellent.! It' funny plying. One more time. Having me, start?

Twenty-four! I tall pig.

Plus, thirty-two. pig have question to me with to me.

Fifty-six, and miners ten, I have told pig.

forty-six and plus twenty-one, I have questioned to pig.

Eighty-seven, and miners thirty-five. so, do I.

Fifty-two! are you funny? I am telling pig. Ok?

Next, one more time, doing?

So, pig moves head up and down.

I am study with book. And have rest viewing in windows did do see that.

In pass on middle morning with birds, clouds, and woods.

In the room full as cycling worm air.

Often Paper of book is one page turn once at that come hearing lightly and ringing sound come from here to my ears, my breath through windows coming here coolly. Windows

Speaking for me in the worm and cool mixed my body come here. after all that is peaceful. Two hours later. I am do be stop study go down stair, and in the kitchen, I have drink worm milk.

Mom will back.! I hurry up go out. My think is far distance take almost two hours. There I will go there now, and before I told my mom about that is you will go village is under mountain, then there I will go that is speaking, Mom allows to me, and mom told me.! you have turn back home in three hours. And mom give me two thousand won.

Mom.! Thank you.

I have exchange as simple wears. I am going out with small bag is water and Lipkin and purse in is money. I go through the narrow road and surround is still brown's green color 'leaf and

Plaints and beautiful flowers so on...

I go up slice deep roads, and go down, vibration with left and right yellow color of flowers by the slice winds. Now this road is flat. And I smoothly pass the road that I see the little widely in be sight. I walk to the go there that village.one more time cool winds blow to me. I have sat on the side flat locks and see Passing sheep side me .by orderly the sheep going with varied line, hi! Jim. Jim is walking by ship. He is under village's boy. He is having cute and slice face. he sees to me, have smile to, he is doing bite seed and seeing me going to mountain with sheep. He questions to me, how are you?

I have smiling be answering to him, fine! Have that, yes!

Aren't you? Me too.

Today is Manu? Bob!

Ok!

How about you?

Soup with meats!

All Right! I am answer.

Where are you going? Jim with having little curious questions to me.

I am going under village to play.

What's play? Jim question to me.

Walk tour....

Right! have nice a day Nancy! Have please walks!

Goodbye!

I get up and walk to village. on walk I am going, I will meet my aunt, my aunt is alone. she is in her house. specially she kind to me, is suavity. Gently. she is having professional writer. Occasion come in my house and talks with mom. she is younger than mom' old, about five years. According to the flat narrow load that road is almost grown small seed side stay ,and that surround red and whiter and green color' s is wildly before and after, up and down ,vibrations , I am going up little slice deep a pave road .the pave lode is made of cement, shoe wearied me is slice be worm, and my face is be change More than more as red, and face being sweat. In the

Sky is very clearly and, I want cry that mind to oneself, and I cry that yahoo I am live! I love mom! nice meet you that!

The sound listened to front of mountains. And once more back to me be sound as her me having love.

For a walk, and I see surrounded with demanding work people in the field. I am going up mountains with cover snows distance from the little narrow road meet and me going the narrow road. I am slowly walk seeing a front of scene roads because.

I am road is ugly and deep and narrows, now, narrows flite is,

Little walk to the front, after moment. One more medium deep road is, I was carefully walking. narrow roadside was stay such as wells forms, going road of is here and there flowers and seed. I once more pear slice deep down roads. Narrow rode, for distance, as soon as narrow road pass, little wide road seen on, I see on side road flat locks, and I am sitting over there. The light come to me slice worm with mixed slice windy and feeling. Over there listen the sounds that birds fly as orderly group in the sky. As much as orchestra, I am little tired.

Over there I see flat rocks, on sleeping, for a moment, overview There I see that people gathering. and I run to the gathering. Group people. there one person selling fruits, agriculture tools, and kitchen tools and vegetables, so on. I have only three thousand won. And answer to person. Could tell me? how is that? the person has answer. me questions that was is fruits that is apples. The apple is one is four hundred won, two is seven hundred won. Three is nine hundred won, could your

Buy that? I am concern that and... I have choice, and tell person Buy three that.! I have given nine won. And receive three apples. Two get in my bag. one is me has eaten.

The person is me has speaking as thankyou and waive hand to me, so do I. I walked slice deep and flat narrow roads going now with seeds stay on the grounds.

6. plant in mind for the futures.

On going four hours than I expected that, about eight hundreds miter remain, I am going sliced down deep going on the roads the road is unpaved with on small ugly rock and miny dust mixed and difficulted to breaths to me. Over there, she seems my aunt's house. that is cover with white painting, which is make of flat wood, next is small warehouse.at Front yard is small groups got at small yard plants in vegetable as strawberry, blueberry, cons. The aunt's house is being surrounding with that Fence be make of flat woods. More than more come on near

the aunt's house. On going to that, seen
be like widely flat road and surrounded
large and small seeds growing, on side
roads that flowers growing on going up
and down, and left and down, my aunt's
house her carry of dogs is. That dog is
spot with darken brown on basic white of
brown. that is gentle and cute. Living in
with my aunt, that house is aunt's house
at next,

Then I am arriving front on that, I call to
the house,

Ant' name is Rola, could have in Rola, with
knock, I am Nancy,

After moment, ant come out.

Oh! Hi Nancy, how do you on here come

on?

I am glad meet you.!

Ant, please have to me.

I am brushing my wears and shoes. And go in the house.

Room in the house is very cozy, in living is softly sofa, and tv, and carpet is basic red on the orange, on the wall is variety paintings and pictures, in the pictures is my mother with aunt and my ant is pass old the process of growth, and grandfather, and grandmother is in family pictures, and aunt's husband and her children. Are you tire? if you come on here, you will tire on. could you have eaten?

She gives me a one class of orange juice,

6

with smalling.

Thank you! I am drink clearly. Delicious.

I had drunk a class. And that hand on to my ant that is Rola. Ant is once more, smile to me. Inside living room fullfed with warm, in house's living room have connected kitchen and bathroom, I go in left bathroom, and have wash hand and face, and have gone living room sits sofa make of leather. I set on next my aunt and little before I had that on load come here, I had bought a silent give my aunt and I are side by side siting that have delicious. What is this? With smile to me question.

Apple before coming here, three buying, one is complete, and remain two. I am sincerely that answer.

My aunt and I each other have talking about to me and concern go on to me. My aunt is talking after gone kitchen. I Take out my bag on the sofa side and silently open the door and get out, Nancy! ongoing out my aunt give me tip. Please, after in thirty minutes get in house. Aunt speaking to me.

Yes! Aunt, I am answer with smile to her. In the front of house is clearly view as much as will be see passing stranger, and in the sky, birds flying and, on the ground, sheep passing that. More at that will be easily see neighborhood 's house. I shortly walking around aunt's house, ongoing road is flat with covered paved as sand rocks that going, at moment I have turn head then I see prettily pretty flower with white and yellow 's color, surrounded with cover tastes smell to me like. After round ten-minute pass, and I go in near warehouse, and I see newly that, that is right, two of horses are, one is white. Another is brown's color; horses and I are firstly, but the horses are gentle. I go near that and my hand on that's head connected body and brushed by brush. And my face is full as smile. as much as in the warehouse is have not smell is clean.

And after I am going in the aunt's house, Rola! I am going in now.! I am speaking to my aunt,

and I am going in bathroom and wash face and hands.

Nancy! dried handguns are on the left shell. Are you get it...

Yes! I was having understood, I am answer with please...

My aunt is having of vegetable soups and bread and reserved worm milk and fresh vegetable and is that mostly on hand harvest. meal table is cover be white color's wear, I am having getting on the chair and eat delicious that. My aunt and I have meal please.

Two we have talked about that mom and me for normal life. Could you live in think your mom is do well?

Aunt questions me, with her face is full curiosity.

Yes! She is very well. I am solely responsible,

Nancy! How do you get more meal.?

No problem! but I need something milk please? I am speaking to her with smile,

Nancy! how do you get here to take long.

About four hours take long. I am shortly talk to her.

When You go on to here, what's matter? Aunt questions me.

No problem!

then I come on here, I am seeing ant see me, inside two apple is empty one classes.

Apples is washing and one have aunt. Other is mine. I am shortly meal before noon have meal. Could I ask to you? I question my aunt.

Yes! You are please!

I wander upstairs and would I go upstairs? I question her.

Yes! Please...

I quietly set up and walk to the front of stair entrance, the stair has made of wood is brightly by the light through windows going into the house. Upstairs have two storerooms. One is my cousin's.

Room has made of forth angle bed and desk. In house well. Cousin's picture with take family and friends and alone. And

that side are painting by himself. on floor
has made of white woods

That is be comfortable to aim in the room.

By desk is book bag with old colors that
token me cousin's older time. On the

Desk pictures, books, pencils, and notes...

And variety form's gears. I moment seeing
surrounding, I go out room, Into the aisle
side, even that is little dusty but most of
be cleaning, perhaps half passing then is
blue color's door making of wood, in
where is cousin's usages playing, that dolls
and bolls, and instrument, and go on...

Hi! Aunt?

Can I give me one piece.?

What' do you see? Ant or crying answer.!

I do like to the instrument!

What kind do you have instrument? Aunt tall me...

I like a horn.

Ok! Nacy! You have one piece, the other, won't you?

I am enough to me.!

If I have a variety that, down stair, and I thankful for give me to my aunt's.

I am getting out with horn. Out of house is widely .at I am shadow by sunshine .be playing horn.

Firstly, sound is bumblebee. Little think is amateur. but then pass times, and I am feeling the sound with natural.

I get in deep pocket that get in the house,

and once more spend doing thank to going at aunt be kitchen.

I love it!

I am glad you have gotten it! Aunt is answering.

In the house viewing out windows still brightening.

7, rising your mine and you have flying.

Special we are going out meal with dogs. Aunt smiles go on to me, outside desk is cover with umbrellas that prevents for me about directly razer. That is our skin and heatstroke to, outside air is freshly, and be normal worm to us. Under viewing, two's Dogs is having meal. One is wildly eating. Other is careful eating. On the ground is flatted pebble in square round meal desk, my aunt is speaking to me.

How about you for meal?

We had meal that was meat soups, breads, and juice and mix sauce vegetables,

It is delicious! My answer with smile, each other.

I love it, my answers.

Side was dogs is having bark to us.

Little Pass afternoon,

Sun shining to us little hot, but I was feeling worm.

We have orderly and cleanly on the desk. I am going in the bathroom, and my aunt is going to warehouse to give meal for houses.

My aunt gives me an apple I get in my pocket and one more time playing horns, the sound is naturally to her,

Her face is full smile with horn's sound. At Long distance that, also with smile speaking to me.

Wahoo! You are excellent player!

The sound was having listen to long distance.

So do I, thank you, my aunt. I will be professional with horn.!

The sound is going to the long ways.

My aunt reserves rest chair for me. And with smile. I am sitting on chair, sleeping with covering blanket. One hour later, I am open eyes. then I am seeing surrounding, mountain still cover with white snow, long away file did grow as a little seed, near house dogs play with each other. Aunt doing washed wear that drying putting on the line by sunshine.

My other hand on picks up horn peacefully. At moment get up. and go in the kitchen and drink juice, still shining to me brightly, has wink with that at time. On windows brown color's birds singing song to me with please. I am going in, to the wash hand and face, and I go in living room to reading books.

There are variety books. I like books about animal. Specially horses, dogs.

After the kind of these books reading, I am going up stair and browser that cousin was did study the works.

Seeing to me have made known about study grown process formal. I found that can read books, which is geography, that before don is have seen that, my mine is as much as riding cloud, I am very happily. I going to the aunt, with book. aunt is cleaning in the kitchen.

Hi Rola aunt!

With full of please. And I ask you to borrow the book.

Where are you get here.?

It is that is my cousin's room. Could you allow me to borrow this book?

What is about book? Aunt carefully questions to me.

That is about geography.

How long take you reading this book?

Perhaps, about taken four hours.

Do so you return to me after one week

later.

Thank you, sir.!

I am playing to the sky with please. My aunt faced with fully smile and seeing me.

I directly walked to the living room, set on the book in my bag. at same time slice cool windy blows side windows. Moment, I see outside through near windows, there also cows seeding seed. Neighborhoods take care of vegetable, then doing pass, hotter sunshine is little and little worm go on be.

That day is I was going on here passing three days ago. I must back home; I carefully question to my aunt.

Rola aunt! I must go home now.!

Well, tomorrow will leave my home.!

Yes.! Aunt...

I am reserve aunt given me horn and lend me book, and on next morning before to start will have that. Neighborhood is going to their home, and in the sky is little and little red, yellow is darker. Surround is only as birds' sound listen.

Nancy!

Why! Rola aunt?

Have dinner?

Ok!

I am change wears and I am going to the kitchen and sitting her front.

What's day today is mane.? I am glade to her.

Its day today mane is meat soupe.!

What kind of meat?

It is gout...!

Gout?

I do not like that.

It is small!

it has made me as that is smoothly and sweetly and do not small...

Ok! Thank you Rola aunt.!

And with milk and breads make that as barley and corn. And vegetables.!

Oh! Have delicious to us... ki.ki.

After I am doing eat, go bathroom, and washing hand and brush teeth. I was going the living room, and I was reading painting books. That is famous person's biography. After reading that. I was feeling amazing in the book. Fleeing cool from windows, my aunt close windows, I little and little going in sleeping. As soon as pass two hours, I wake up, and seeing around, next sofa aunt having crochet with blue thread. I rub my eyes by hand. And get up, going to upstairs, there was my cousin stayed room, I am lay on the bed and see celling that is did made of flat wood. Each other connected orderly. Specially, because floor and ceiling side is wildly deep, the rooms are very widely. Cold and chilling air is fulling in the room. I am little and little sleeping now.

Good night! Rola aunt!

Me too.!

Still windows out is lightning bright start.

In the dark night sky

As Dark blue color is set in deeply. The color is do not image, and God is having created university' only ones. That is me do not listen to the sound, seeing, we can feel that seen that. Their love,

Man's emotion to.

In the morning, I get up with wash face and hand.

Aunt is cooking on kitchen with two dogs.

Today to start early reserve meal,

Good morning Rola aunt?

Good morning ...

My aunt busy in the kitchen with cooking.

In the kitchen room is two dogs, I am playing outside house with that. The sun is East rising, the shining is on slice wet ground, with brightly eyes. as drawn is that my surround is slice wetted, that is feeling cooling. My foot moves busy there and here. Following the dogs that I did.

Passing five minutes and my body rise as perspiration, but my mine is feeling cleaning. Dogs feeling do that. In the house aunt calling me. I am hurry up going in the house. And I am going bathroom to shower. Change wear and go in the kitchen and I see my aunt.

Have delicious, my cut!

Thank you, aunt!

What's menu.?

Today morning menu is kimbap. Aunt has answer.

Oh, incredibly good, that is my very favorite menu.

How do you go on?

Now! Here,

Thank you, aunt!

Have your testes that firstly?

Yes! I am answering and kimbap get in my mouth, and feeling be sweetly.

Aunt stays care a kimbap in my bag, I am quietly going out. Dogs in the hose out to guard me. Two dogs please bark to me.

Aunt' house to back, I am going to my house. I am happy. because I am fully, and

I have kimbap and apples. Came here then rode and return rode is different each other, to the house that is very please and to the aunt's house road is curious and have hope. I must go almost four hours. slice deep hill pass, and face the seen that stranger, and sheep guider is that Wii be seeing, surround is covering green plants. Seed. And fresh air is passing my face and have face downing sweat from forehead. About thirty-minute pass then one person walks to me, normal wearing the man ask to me,

Excuse me? May I ask to you?

I am being fulling curious with, no problem!

How long take time going to next country?
Perhaps. thirty minutes. I now go now!
Set head of red cap the man bows to me
and speaking thank you very much!
I am seeing the man going to country. On
small flat rock I am sitting, and I have
eaten an apple. And have water one
classes one more time passing cooling
windy. Ma head see to the sky, there is
small. And big birds fly to.
I thoughtless sir hand with up and down.
The birds orderly fly to.
Over mountain, sun is rising about middle.
That slice shining does be wormy for my
body. I am going up the slice deep hill on
that surround with the grown green seeds.

I see go on that brown color's bird singing on the tree's sick. I thoughtless take out my horn in my bag. And playing horn. My horn sound and beside birds' sound with did mix, hearing to me harmony sounds. After pass two hours to three hours then I face to narrows road, I go up carefully to this narrow road, one more.

Narrow down road seeing. The road is very wildly. And I hardly walk.

On the road. Sometime a walk, my breath hearing sound with up and down, thirty minutes have passed. Little walking. I see.

That I could have rest area that is little flat rock.at There, I am did have eaten apples and kimbap, kimbap is cooling but unbelievably delicious, to me.

Next small flat field is. And I lay on the field. On Surround softly seed by, do to me sleeping, fresh air and clean mind mixed my body is as much as must flying.

The shinny 's warm and seed's softly do me comfortable,

After passing fifty minutes

I get up on the seed field and walk to my house.

Over there seen my house, my mom is.

I am walking to slice flat and narrow rode, and I am drinking water little. Near have approach my house, mom is in the house suddenly go out, to me, with opening the white made of wood door.

Hi mom! I speaking to her.

Hi Nancy! Mom is face with small, and speaking to me,

Hurry up! Get here, "come in now."

My mom and I am each other have talking about for three days doing that out of house and arrive in aunt house and at aunt's house I have doing a variety works.

I am tired, mom?

That is alight! Let' go in the room. "And have rest you are."!

And going in my bedroom have rested my mind that she did tire my long picnic.

Finishing long journey and come here that my mom's breath. Freely and comfortable.

I am going to bathroom and washing

hand and face and have shower.

On the sky is still brightly and I am gone in bedroom, there are that she waits for me.

Hi pig.

Thank you for me wait for me.!

More time my face is brightly.

How do you do that out?

Outs side is widely, and beautiful flower is fully, and cleanly air and kind peoples, near any people is not. Come and here, my mind is healthy, and be sleeping quietly.

Between the clouds viewed starts is brightly much as in my mind is comfortable rest connected relation with mom' care for me in the sky.

8. have image to the oneself on toward ahead

I get up early in the morning, I had been arrived at home then my Rola aunt give me that, I did let it be the inside conner my bags, in the bag is horn and book. I orderly take out, and on the drawer staying, and once more had sleeping.

One hour after, I open my eyes, my mom is kitchen, at there doing cooking, I am playing horn taking in the drawer, the sound is going out over my windows widely,

May be the sound that listening that have

seeding cows and plants, and birds, near my house be slice wetted by slice rain,

Sometime, wetted and cooling windy blooms to side of windows, I have come on little chilly feeling, pig is still smile for me.

Nacy! have meal!

Yes, I am here now. I am getting up!

I am going berth room and face wash and hand, go to the kitchen,

Nacy! Change your Clouse?

All right! I am once more at my room going, have exchange wears.

Have delicious my cute?

Thank you, mom!

Today is morning meal being fish soup!

Carefully, have meal!

Yellow green colors' soup stays on the white cycling plates, I am sir the soup by my silver colors' spoon, and set in my mouth, I had a feeling in my mouth sweet taste,

I have fully!

And I drinking orange juice,

I love it.!

Mom is seeing me with smiling.

Have me talking to me that story, you have been going aunt' house please?

I have very curiosity. And very funny!

Aunt is very kindly and gentle, meal is good.!

Horse is two on the house, and incredibly

beautiful. Aunts give me that is horn and kimbap and borrow to me cousin' book, which must return in six days, and meal delicious!

Nacy is speaking to her. After morning meal, she is holding horn and that getting go out of house. out is peaceful and fresh air and slice wetted leaves and seed is that told me. I am playing horn. And one time, and two times, and so many times, occasionally playing horn I am more than more be family.

My horn's sounder is going out widely over mountain and trees and over neighborhood house, long away distance viewing, birds sound, and my playing sound are to be harmony. Shortly walks go to the narrow loads, surround is still being wetted by drawn rains.

At moment I am rest on the flat rack. And one more time I walks in the narrow road. In the sky is small pets, that here and there together, come in and out.

As soon as narrow road passing, I did see ever little widely roads. Right the road! I am thinking to go garden, I am interesting the garden, because I have not seen ever there.

There is well cared trees and beautiful chairs and roads.

I am running to the that having horn by right hand. After moment being view for me the beautiful sight. My breath is smoothly. for a walk one three miter, right sit down on the bench, I am slowly seeing that before I do not see sight, which is so on,

I am sitting on the bench with covered tree's shade, which is very cool.

I am quietly that closed my eyes. and falling in sleeping.

In the garden side come here that windy is fleeing flower's smell. Worm sun shiny to me. Near to me is white and yellow butterfly fly to up and down smelling flower' scent, spring's worms' season is developing growth times, and mate each other times. Their wing is beautiful with variety colors is red, blue, white, yellow, brown so on.

After going and backing, Nancy is realizing house's important and mom's love'...

Horn rhythm with Wind's sound mixed in my minds, sometime.

Be west blowing to me, my mind with the sound is doing be same.

Set up on do make of wood with white bench, I walk on dark white marble paved narrow loads. With side in the roadside, Small and cute size flowers is and listening toward to me that grass bug sounded in the side flowers. After, I am arrived garden fountain in that spurt of water with brilliant right reflected by sunshine, that water closed my mouth, I am feeling cooling and refreshing, the fountain has made of variety form's curve on the marble, wind blooms still slice for me.

Over there are mountains, top of that is not have snow and, now at top is green color's trees have been seeing to me. Mountains of side lines is narrow waters is falling to down, there is small lack on the that is variety birds playing on the water. The mountains are still cows seeding.

In the garden I am staying is high and big street trees. One is triangle forms and others are variety forms.as little time as, that vibrations up and down, left, and right slice windy, as with shadows by sunshine.

I am for a walk there and where, my horn sound and with birds and windy sounds together and comfortable prior noon sleep sound, on like listening to me.

After moment, passing a roe deer with basic brown color spotting dark white colors, which is medium size's and, in the nose, rise white wet breath sound, and often walks and runs. Alone going suddenly stop front of me and nose out sound speaking to me.

Hi! deer?

My name is Nancy!

Nice meet to you! I am speaking to deer.

Deer's head moving up and down, I like

made you name!

Your name is `dirs.'! how about you?

It is in `dir.' that noun means dir. is respect.

and `s' is much that,

How about Dir-s?

The roe deer's nose is slice contacted my hand and smell my hand and I am brushed roe deer's back and go in the forest.

I am swing hand to the roe deer, and speaking to a roe deer,

Goodbye dirs..! have next times to me!

Deep growth morning's times, I am feeling worm's shining and

With cooling winds slice my face passing by. Surround is often listening be harmony pets' sounds,

Pass by one person walks on the garden.

Old is little elder than me, may be two years old more,

Hi! The man is speaking to me.

Nice meet to you! Sir! I am response that bow,

It is nice a clean day! I am speaking to him.

Yes! It is funny day.!

Have nice a day. He is leaving the words to me, at bench crossed road to the directly going for a walk.

He is wearing blue pants and white suit that harmonize in the garden with forest.

On my pocket get out my horn, and in my

mouth out breath,

The sounds are fast, modem, slowly, widely over garden going to the surround, I am happy always that play horn, it my cousin was to have usage that, may be, my aunt gives me that, be thankful my aunts, the sound is my face and that touches slice windy, I am feeling as little literature poets.

I am playing that, do, le, me, fa, sol, la, se, do, one more time, do, le, me, fa, sol, la, se, do,

I have practiced the member of playing the horn, and go on, more have more, that is interested in sounds by paying horn, on the that do my fingers have up and down, and I do the Holl closed and opening by fingers.

What do I play singing song.? I speaking to me,

The first is that I do have easily! That all right!

May be, as I will be plying from the 'school bell.' I am thinking that,

One more time, sol, sol, la, la, sol, sol, me, sol, sol, me, me, le,

do things I have playing horn.

That was very carefully and quietly,

After moment, my playing is very family to me,

The sound is listening long away there,

I am on the bench sitting up, and I go to

toward the fountain,

Then I am reach that, I have eats waters rising to the up.

It is very cool, that I am fleeing,

I got bag in, I take that handkerchief, and clean my hand and rose.

two hours passing, that I was out of my house.

I am turning to the house; my right hand is still gripped horn.

On the walk, I see surrounded area cover with corns' color is dark green, my hand streeting toward to leaves, and swing on the that, my feeling vivid the corn's live,

On the windy winds is on the toile in my eyes and I am care me. I am feeling little comfortable, on the going on the house is full of dusty, after moment. I am rightly rising head and, sight have seen to me my house,

Mom! I am here,

I am with glade crying to mom in the kitchen,

Mom is cooking and speaking to me.

Have go in! and wash and change wear!

Yes! Mom!

I am directly going in the bathroom, and wash my face and my hand, and exchange my wears. My horn is in my pock that transfer to another pocket. And go in living room in I am sleeping quietly.

Two hours later, I am wake up then, my

mom is calling to me.

My cute! Could you go down kitchen.!

Yes! Mom! I am stretching my arms, and blanket ordering, go to go down.

On the meal desk is orange juice and cookies.

Mom! Thank you for me to delicious deserts! I send my mom.

Words.

Mom, how do you do then I am absent?

Yes. I have reading books. And newspaper and work out front of house file and playing with dogs and knitting, so on....

And Nancy! How do you do aunt house?

whom... I am shortly thinking,

Speaking to the mom,

I am reading books and seeing horses, and for a walk surround front of aunt's house,
Mom is involve seeing to me,
and more?
I am delicious meal, before me arrive to my home, variety meals have reservation for me.
It is a nice full; I am answer to her.
And aunt gives me horn and lend me cousin's book.
Mom is smalling on the face to me.
Out windows are still brightly shiny in my house,
Mom! Could you go out allow for me?
Yes! Have it!

Nancy is don's normal, but she goes out her house!

Once more I set on toile, I am feeling is very more comfortable than I was aunt's house.

Sometime sparrows fly in my front on house and come out.

Sametime, in blue color's sky birds varietally flying out on my head.

Mom? Having me!

I am going in my bedroom, and, made of wood, that stair footing, and go up.

Heading front on white door, I am bowing my friend's pig.!

Hi! Pig!

Come here! Pig is answer to me, and I

open my room's door.

How long been here for see you?

Pig is smiling to me,

Pig! Could you play game with me?

Ok!

What's game is today.?

Today is hospital game.! Pig told me.

Pig! You are doctor! I am patient. Ok? I am speaking to the pig.

What's problem to you? Pig speaking doctor.

I am problem is headache.

What are your symptoms cycling the headache? Pig is speaking to me,

It a weak up in morning, aching that. I am speaking pig.

Headache is variety reason, example, have meal, body utility problem, problem to the shocking about in or out, so on,

May be if you will be stress forms 's headache, pig is speaking to me,

Could you tell me, what's resolve way to me have doing? I am telling pig.

May be, I am giving you medicine, and you must take that cycling.

 two per one day, no problem in take time. You must reminder that cycling. And in the morning, you must get up early and for a walk. Pig is speaking to me.

And you must get meal with fresh vegetable cabbage, carrot, onion, so on...

Dir, my headache, is it not a big problem?

Pig is seeing smile to me, with care for me.
Dir pig thank you so much! I am
understanding your answer did solve that.
I am quietly going out in the doctor room
and get medicine in the dispensary. The in
hospital still quiets, and I am out there,
Pig swing hand for me,
I am dip on the desk and crossing arms
under head, I am sleeping little,
When I am wake up my sleeping. On had
stay pig was fall on side.
I am sorry pig. I am rightly pick up that,
staying on the side desk,
Pig! shall we study today?
I like geography, pig is answer for me.
Yes! I do!

Could have me first contents is that? I am question to pig.

How about is that our country area!

That is surround with mountains, and plants in toile, widely field and on the ground is trees and each of houses, and at little distance is narrow water into the rocks, and variety, plants get in the field and near in living we are staying in the house.

Mountain name, country name, load name, in the area is, historical site so on,

First, is me stay here?

I am staying in the house! Pig having curious answer to me.

Well, I question to you! what is country

name that we are riving now? West province! Pig is answer to me.

Next country name is that is west province Jony, pig is smile to me.

And what side rode is name over there?

Silly hill! Pid is crying to me,

pig and I were funny. After silently feeling, I am one more time question to that.

How long Is we stay here original?

Thirty years is old.

Who is Here first man?

Who is living over there hill, his name is john stive,

All Right! I am answer to that thankful about respond pig.

I have finished the work!

I am folding that book, and I think to writing daily diary.

Another book browsing, and...

9. handy your hands for each other from like...

Nancy! Do have a breaktime!

Yeh, mom!

I am going down satire and directly to the kitchen.

Hello! Mom, what's today dessert menu?

Today menu is barley bread and orange juice.

I am sitting down chair and seeing meal desk that is yellow, brown's color has delicious,

Thank you, mom! I must well be,

Into my mouth and sweetly mixed with

juice are doing.

My right hand hold one classes of juice and other hand is pork,

Sometime barley bread chewing, I am feeling sweetly.

Nancy! What do you have meal after.?

Mom, I will have to play back yard with my friend.

How take playing long?

May be one hour taking to play.

I am all sum, and go out into the back yard, out is still worm by sunshine, seeing around a walking guess with yellow, and white color's bodies orderly going to the narrow water.

They sound to me as Quique, that me on

sound listening, coming please that, after passing guess with smiling, the footage is clean leave statue, to me.

When I am reaching my friend's fence of front, neighborhood's father is training horse, then I am calling his father,

Have you seen here john? His father is smiling to me,

Yes! He is out of house, he had gone down to country,

Perhaps, will be pass noon lately.

Thank you having me! I am responding to him, and going to the quiet forest with seed as my high growing and siting on the flat lacks,

I am taking it, and brash my face with

perspiration, for a long, about twenty minutes, I am seeing the front of mountains. The mountains are covering as green color, and more than more be on change to the dark green from down to head, on the face shiny sunshine is little more than yesterday, but I am resting to shadow under seed's leaves. It is very cool and very quietly comfortable to me. Chilly windy sometime booming to my face

I am taking out my horn from my pocket, and as handkerchief, behave washing, to brightly.

That I was playing the school bell, I will play,

The horn is through the cycling hold bar

that's sound is clean and gentle sounds going widely.

I am staying inside is on rise steam through going up small pets is ants, they orderly are having oneself gathering, up and down, the ant's bodies are reflecting by sunshine to going out brightly. The many of them are deep brown, others are almost black. I am rise to my head up and seeing that the small pet is grasshopper on inside connect on stream of middle is side little green spotted yellow browns' colors. That slowly going up. Suddenly, to head up seeing, the cons' leaf on middle top by sunshine that did bright my eyes, and my eyes is grimace.

At did shade that there, my head down to the seeing ant closely. At moment rest under shade, surround is quietly and cooling with

On my head is middle dried sweat by windy booming to my face.

I get up that stay, I am going to the back yard. There is very widely yard to playing that running exercise to my healthy. Ere I have try running,

Then I am running that my breach is listening sounded my mouth and noise is dancing up and down roughly.

Downing my head and I am globing my horn to right hand,

I was thinking, I have back my house, and

running to the house,

Mom! Go in,

After I am shower and go upstairs and did be sleeping quietly.

My mom is still sitting on chair reading newspaper.

After pass about one-hour, deep sleeping is wake by my mom' calling for me,

My cute! Wake up!

I am getting up on bed, hi! Pig, are you rest in during in dreaming?

Pig is smiling for me, and hi! Nancy! glade meet you, and to me, gently sent words.

I am gone directly down stair. There already reserve meal for us. Mom sitting front of meal desk,

Hi! Mom.

Hi! My cute! Mom is reserving to start have meal!

Are you ready? Mom is smiling me.

Ok! I like it! I am glad to me and to my love it my mom. Mon send that me and have it.

mom and I quietly meal, mom question me. Nancy? you have meal after, how do you do?

I will study with books on my room. I am answering the question,

I told my arms crossing and I am seeing my mom. Mom is slice smiling to me.

I am set up on the chair and go in my bedroom, in bedroom still pig is on the desk to me, on smiling, hi! pig!

May I ask to you?

Whatever ask to me!

Do we have playing study?

No problem!

Could you think playing something?

Before, we had doing something.

Moo,

A- ha! Geography!

Ok!

Let us study now! I am speaking pig.

We have country name before, pig is answer about that,

I love it.

As I am answer to that,

Today are geography two classes. That is

playing game!

How about you? If I speaking to the country name calling,

That next, you must have to first name's nouns, you must have to speaking that,

Example, if I am calling to hanging's first name! you must have to that answer, as Hoge you are answering. And connect you are calling `Hoge,' as last noun you calling to me, and you are answers is eerie calling to me.

Are you understanding?

Yes, I am understanding, pig is answering, with smiling to me.

I am first calling to you.

'Seoul'! `first noun'! I am calling to pig.

`Sejong'! last noun! `Yongsan! pig is calling to me!

That is last noun! I am answer that.

`Nang' is last noun! I speak to pig.

`Kyungzoo' is last noun! Pig speaks to me.

 Over window slice windy come on here, I open my book, and in deep sleeping be doing, after one hour, I am open the eyes, my books once I see, and once more, as soon as I am flat the page, I am into the deep thinking and in care. Do you have known the contents, you do not' know that do you understand in the book's contents.

I am little fold, and I am going downstairs, in the living room mom is sleeping with cover blanket, holding her hand by newspaper I am quietly in the room, going to diner room, and

On the Dinner desk I take juice, and pure getting in the glass,

Drinking In my mouth that, my tongue feeling sweet send me.

My mind, and go out,

Over there is coming on my house rain, windy is more than I am thinking, I am back, and go in my house.

I am going my bedroom. And have closed windows that nearly opening, out is chilly with winds and rain, but into the room is comfortable and cozy. I am back my desk and open my books.

I am thinking 'what's book seeing that,'

That is Mathematics!

Ok! Pig!

In that is plus and miners, division, and multiplication and...

First! One plus one is two! Ok!

Second! one miner one is zero!

I am slowly learning by oneself that.

As more as studying the mathematics I am being involved that.

After two houre, I am going to bathroom and wash hand and face, drinking one classes of juice in the kitchen,

Mom! could you do I outside going allow?

well! You do have Your thinking,

thank you, mom! I will like outside now.

Just moment! how long outside staying?
May be, Two hours long.
I have exchanged my wears, and other
hand hold a horn.
Backyard is cover with little black clouds
coming on my head slowly perhaps, will
be rain. I have sited outside the white
house, on the ground black, brown color's
ant going to the house orderly, take out
my horn in my pocket. And my mouth
blooming in the hole entrance, and listen
the sound,
The sound is doing long away widened.
The sound is deeply for me peacefully and
silence little more,
I see surround that is worm shine is still

beam for me, near is con's stream toward to up has green color's lines is on the dark green basic, feeling Colden by a little rainy fall on my head. I am going in my house. I think that will pass rainy, but more than more falling that,

Mom! I am going in!

Dry your hair and body. And change your wears. Mom has told me teacher.

I am going into the bathroom wash face and hand and change my wears. And going kitchen, have drinking worm milk that is mom is doing reserved after noon desert. Milke is sweetly. I am rest on the meal desk's chair, and I go to the bedroom there is my mom, and I am lay on the softly dark yellow leather sofa that is smell sweetly with wood scent. Sofa's spring bound made me cool and comfortable, near me is mom is singing song, I am fall in sleeping by the sound.

Do well, be sleeping my baby.

My mom is knitting my wear,

 two hours, I am open the eyes and slash my eyes by my hand. Mom is kitchen to the cooking for me.

But, passing Hi! Nancy, could you wash hand?

Yes! I am responding that. And I am going in the bathroom.

My mom is busy to cooking and set to meal on the table.

After I am wash, I am going in the kitchen and sit on the chair.

Two's hand strains my face under, and I am smiling to mom.

Mom! Today is menu.

Today is menu being kimbap, before days, we have eaten,

Mom is nice, good for that!

Thank you cute!

First, I have eaten that, kimbap is black color's, in that is bap and variety vegetables and sausage, go on...

After that eaten, I am drinking milk.

My face is to be healthy.

Mom is seeing my face with smile, and mom's face is gentle and peaceful.

10. in the sitting down on the chair and reading books.

Going in my bedroom and aunt lent me book have open,
The book' name is geography, one by one I turn over the page.
In the page is variety contents, us 's nation and world's locals.
Feature, and nature. Interesting to me, the contents is the local's name is interesting for me, as I am flapping the page, I was feeling did have learn many that is historical, culture, custom, that my knowledge was more widely, moment I am see outside into the windows, there is still

white color is basically blue color,

I am folding the book and take out horn

in my pocket,

My mouth contacts horns on head and

playing that 'school bell.' The sound is

cheerful to me and the surround in my

house turn cycling.

Out of windows is still sun is shining to

me as worm. Deep afternoon is passing

and I the afternoon's comfortable be

feeling easy my body.

I am playing one more time, and one

more is 'wild rabbit,' in my horn's sound

come on the listening song that by man is

sing song,

sometime, the windows are going slice

vibration with sound by windy, after playing the horn, I take in my bag that, and I am pick out in my bag a book, that book's name is mathematics.

I am interesting mathematics, sometime, under more once per a day I am reading the book, the book is full basic known teaching me that I did not know the contents.

I am reading book after, I am more and more be sleeping, sometime out is still chilly windy blooming to my house's windows, in the living room my mom is reading the newspaper.

Passing two hours, I brush me on eye by my hands and I get up on the chair, I get out to living room.

Hi! mom?

Could you ask for question that?

Yes! What is about for that question!

Could you we have dog? I am question to her.

Why?

Aunt's house is care of two of dogs. Because The dos is smart and cute. And I want care of dog.

No problem that,

May be on the two block long neighborhoods are care of dogs I am going to that and must please and get two's dogs or buy the dogs in that.

How about you that?

Mom! That ok! I am answers that.

I am drinks juice and go out.

Out is after raining, which is wetted as slice campers on being painting by water and paints mixed. After moment, I am walking through the narrow road, my breathe come in clean air. As soon as breaching. I am delight because my minds are healthy feeling to me by that. On the ground is cover with wetted, and brightly by side clouds shine from on the dark brown sky.

I am walking to along slice wind come to me. Each other seeing windy and my face. It is cool, at long away is bird's together that each other eating meal and fly to the sky orderly.

Moment after going, I am arrived garden, garden becomes my favorite area, long away seen the bench, I am running to that, and sit on the bench, I am taking out a horn that my ant gives to me, I had playing. The playing is name's 'you rise me up' but it is little difficulty, I once playing that, its song's story is that your praise is my braves.

During I am playing horn, passing man see me once by their eyes. As soon as I am playing song, my mind is feeling as flying. My front, one's dog is coming, I have made one passenger is that I am please and delightful! I am playing go on, the passenger goes out still. My music is widely going toward the long away. And in areas, the garden is full my music, sometime come here yellow basic brown spot birds.

The bird is smile cute to me, I am glade to that, I am thinking to the playing that, next is 'from love,' that is normally song, which is Korean crowd normal song,

That song is going long away and widely going out. My passenger was still crowding around my side and front.

As soon as I am playing the horn, that is fly another place. I am set in pocket the horn. When I was going outside, I was have come out, glove the candy of that is take out and, set in my mouth, I am feeling sweetly. Because This area is do not see the sea. That is long away from my house there is distance almost two hundred miles away my house. I want to see the sea.

Only seeing in the books, if I have chance see the sea, I will see the that.

One more time horn in my pocket, and playing horn, this time is name is `wood.' I am playing that please.

One more time, be gathering passenger. The passenger is come and out to front of me. They are growing with natural environment. And pure and innocent, but do not likely man is do pollution natural, we must do care of natural, and preserve that,

Pass two hours, I am set up on the bench, and go to the my house being foot on the ground, the road is pave with little rocks and come on cover with toils, surround is quietly as little baby sleeping, cons is near growth, in that seen yellow color's cons is each other contacted, stream, and leaves in side are going out brushes. my hand doing stretch and stir with swing contact con's stream. Often that is doing vibration by windy. That windy is pass my face, it gives to me slice cooling, and give me freshly mind, on walking I see the sky, that sky is on blue colors is doing spot to white color's clouds, nearly reached my house,

Mom! could I am going in?

I am doing wash hand and face, and go to the living room, there is my mom. Mom is reading books, I quietly question,

Mom? I am going in!

Mom is smiling for me,

How do you do outdoor?

I am walking and playing horn in outdoor.

Are you funny?

Yes! I am.!

When I am playing, very many passengers crowd for me.!

What is it?

Passenger?

Yes!

Passenger is birds! I am smiling for mom.

Nacy! Have meal!

Yes! Mom, what is today's menu?

Specially! Have meat! Mom is cry for me stressful.

Mom! I like meat and vegetable, both likely. I am mannerly to mom.

I and mom are going to kitchen each other. And mom prior made that take out and set to front of me.

On the table is kimchi, bop. Source. Cooked meat, nearly set I have meal well. Thank you, mom.! I am speaking to her.

Meal is going to mouth; I am feeling sweetly. Specially meat, which is consists of source that is on the pen, after it preheat, that go in the pen and heating,

After I have a meal, I am drinking milk, Mom?

I have all sums.! I am speaking to mom!

After I am brushing my teethes. I go out outdoor.

Out is little doing well for a walk.

11. always remember yourself on freshy minds save memory.

I am wake early in the morning; sleeping is amazingly comfortable.

My friend fig?

Have a nice day.! Nancy!

What's Today is playing? I am questions to pig.

How about a school playing?

Yes! How do you play? I am curious about playing that.

I did explain to you that.

Firstly, you are teacher, and I am student.

That is easy!

Other is each other must be speaking in

school related contents,

Let us start.!

Pig is going in class, student is mine, is sitting on the desk,

One person is sitting up, and cry to the student,

attention! and bow!

In the class is students speaking to the pig.

Good morning, sir! That listening, speaking to them.

Good morning! Nice meet you!

Today is what have learned page?

It is one hundred two pages, please open the books.

It is time is historical.

The page is American historical,

America have been to start be creations that and developing and war and reaching today is the most powerful nation of other nation, one-hundred-page contents is American's development, the page is in that American's immigrations and staying and life, adventure, and development.

What is it.!

teacher to me and historical found.so on.

Hi teacher! I am rising one hand and,

I am questions to sir!

How do America become powerful nation?

That is. Moment pass. That is challenge.

The sprite is challenge.

And faith sprite!

Pig is speaking to student,

I am understanding that, with deep face is go up fleeing to the smiling.

Now we must learn the points! Pig is powerfully speaking for me,

I am listening to me about that, American's historical is interesting and funny, it as much as if I see cinema for me. Hi! Nancy! have desert! Mom is calling me. This is desert is if it is later having meal, but it is going out ahead meal, today specially.

Yes! Mom! I go in the living room. There are cookie and one glass of milk, I am surprising seeing mom.

Aha that is desert will give to you because bop is lately did boil. Thank you, mom, I

must well eaten meal. After desert, I am
going up stair is my pig. and next to
connecting playing,

Hi, student! if you have questions, you ask
to me, pig is speaking to me.

I like to know the America's famous
peoples. I am speaking to teacher.

Pig is smiling for me.

The present is Abram Lincon. He is
American's sixteen president, he works
nations united the north and south
province,

Are you understand? Pig has told me that.
and story is gone on to the deeply for me.

And destroyed slavery. Human is do not
relative face colors. Human is equality

about of all people. Pig is eagle that's mouth. And slice see me.

Also, he is leave for us a famous word that is 'of the people, by the people, for the people.

My two eye is little closed by tired, then my mom is calling me,

Nancy, have meal! you have morning meal!

I was folding the book, run into the kitchen,

In the kitchen is rice set in bread, and be cooking meat, mixed variety season, set in bread. And the next is juice and source with sweetly season,

I was finish meal and I am walk out is back yard.

My house is white color's bench, at there is my mom was resting space.

I am going to that and sitting down the space. That is comfortable, worm with cooling windy is bloom to me, after moment I am doing sleep on the bench. Still that windy is come on my face, shine beams me hotly. Sometime as move as I am listening to bench's unbalance sounds, my shoes did make of leather's dropped on the ground, another is have taken off oneself, mid morning's coz is please for me because I am feeling for that is peaceful.

My mom is out of the house because my mom's personal work to family. Long away is markets. And my mom is going by horses. On going is take two hours.

Hi! Nancy!

Yes! Mom?

I will be going to the in country and take care of our house!

Yes! Mom! I am responsible to talks.

I once more go in and take horn and sitting on bench.

What's play is playing song? Oneself on speaking to me,

It is `do re me song' I am begin playing horn. The sound is wake to me. Still mid-morning shine was reflecting to me warmly.

I am waling for around my house, many

plants are growing on the yard, I am stretching my hand to the plants' leaves.

And of that is one has cut, and it goes in my mouth. The taste is sweetly and little bitter, in my mouth is fully informal with both mixed. The leaves are coming on me with shake and touching my face softly.

Plant' top is such a pin that touch me with swing by slice windy.

I am rest in my house two hours and at outside, call me by my mom.

Hi! Nancy!

I am going in the house. Mom's hand weight two's pup

Nany! How do you do about that? one is white, and another is brown. both is each other is male and female.

It is wonderful. I am likely happy.!

Could you with me made dog's house at out?

Yes! Mom!

Mom tides the puppy on the bench leg. And pick up woods.

Variety material being usage, after thirty minutes, making that dog's house.

Mom!

Could you give me making dos's name?

Whom... Mom is taking long time to make dog name.

How about White color is josh and brown color is Jody.?

Ok! Mom!

Mom is nearly making that is josh and Jody 's house.

The house is likely my house color that white.

Their house is plate unused blanket.

Mom and I going in my house.

I am getting in bathroom with my mom, have wash hand and face, brushes my hair by hand, mom is with me, mom is smiling with me,

Mom, could me let out now?

No problem! Nancy! Mom is gently speaking to me,

I am open the door my house and go to the yard, outside is current still worm shine and worm windy each crossing to my face, as soon as I am walking through on to the do not paved road, I am feeling send me rock's ugly, the over there is flat rock before then I was rest that, I am on the flat rock, in my pocket taking out hand cape, clean my face, and I going the near stream that sound listening currency water sound, sometime fast or slowly see to me, the steam is cooling and chilly, I am on the small cycle rock, and in the steam is small fishes, that 'name is rich fish, they is gathering move on the target aim to oneself go to that.

Side stream is small rabbit that is two, one is white, and another is dark white, two is rest nearly each other. I am care go to them, they involved themselves into the work. After moment, they leave along stream side slowly.

Sunshine is worm to me more than more, at there I wash face and watering, so do I go up along stream, my head touch passing on the plant's leaves, soon going I am feeling my head is dew is rising. Thirty minutes passing, I was rest under plants' leaves.

Windy sometime come and outing. I have taken my horn in my pocket; the sound is going over there is back to me become eco.

Once more, windy blow to me slice.

I am sitting on the flat rock near stream, I

am thinking my mom.

Mom is devoting to me about all thing, and I thank to my mom.

Perhaps it is certainly mom, so do I, good mom will be.

Once more take horn in my pocket, once again playing song.

If I have grown, what's man will be?

That is 'hi wood! Hi wood!'

The song is very deeming mean to me,

The song is that hi wood hi wood hi winter wood, at shade cover with snows, alone standing, nobody does not come here being finds at cool winter, along wind, may be do blow only loose rhythm.

This song is very cheerful for me. my mind

was to be gentle.

Sometime Surround is listening bird's calling each other, is quietly.

I did get in pocket the horn. And stand on the rocks, side is currency water in narrow water have cleaning and pure, I am walking side in that listening rolling dew on waters. In the sky is very clearly with white, blue color draws on the green sea.

With wind's cooling breath did breathe is come in my nose, and one more come out to worm breath.

I am seeing to down and pick up small stone with bright and dark white color, I am once exam the stone, and thrown the plated on the water' surface, the stone is flying to the on the away water surface with brightly by sun.

I walk following narrow water line. On the ground is stay ugly and variety form's small stone is fleeing press and me under foots and touching my leather shoes.

Long away come here, I seen the sky with white, blue color.

There are still flying birds on, I am once closer my eyes, because sunshine going in my eyes.

I stopped to stay on the side narrow water, go up the road, the road is dry and most of dusty, side near seen plants,

My leather's shoes with moister and dusty is mixed.

Little wet mixed my clothes and worm shines. I thank that I will go back home,
I am walking long along the road, naturally my wetted wear and shoes have been by worm air. Side rode accidently, I meet my neighborhood uncle. He is picking up fishes to cooking,
A head me bowing to him,
Hi! Uncle!
Nice a meet you?
Have do you stay on the house? I am question carefully him.
Yes! He does well be.
How about you with Jody do well to your friendly?
He is questions me about he and me

meet frequently.

No! he is busy? I am question him about what's work doing now?

He is out the house; he is learning the horse training now. He is very excellent, I did that. How about his rest time?

I must talk about that he is now learning that each other.

Perhaps he is my house, in warehouse.

Would you like me join the work? I am sincerely question him.

No problem. But I am promise him about rest time and work time, that with talking and after I will tell you, maybe he is resting in warehouse.

Thank you very much uncle, latter see you

again!

Uncle is going swing hand with smile and go over there.

Then one of gathering is come here to seed. Others is fly to the sky with slice dark blue, one is shortly fly to the sky.

Passing two hours I thinks that I must go back to the home. On going slowly, I get out my pocket hand Scarfe and clean my face and neck, I am seeing on the side under road that is narrow water side made by wet toile and seed and broken rock mixed each other. I am little going to the front and footing wet and dry ground and go to on the road, the small road pass widely sight has doing seeing to me, side rode is blooming flower and plants is growing and I am going to the lake. There are birds drinking water and each other talking, I am sitting on front of lake, from that blown to me, I am feeling the cooling windy of lack surface, my hand gets in the lake, my hand stirs left and right, over and under water surface. The birds fly on the that must pick up dew. I am rising on the front lack. And

I am walk along flower's side and from those be feeling to me that is sweetly.

12. always your greenly mine be memory.

Already, the sun is on my head, nearly I am reaching my house,
Mom is hanging wears on the line. Noon's shine beams eagle to me.
Nancy!
Yes! Mom?
Have wash and meal!
Yes! Mom!
Mom is busy to her works.
I am once more seeing my mom and go in the house, go in and I am washing my face and hand, and change my wears. Hand craft is by handing wash and sweat with wears I wash my hand and send to

my mom.

Mom is smiling to me. oh! Cute!

Twenty-minute latter, mom is going in the kitchen, and question to me.

What's today is menu? Nancy!

Bread! I am crying soundly.

Excellent! I have will give you meal! Please wait for minute, mom tall me simply.

I am waiting for, I am humming in my mouth, really, fun wait time.

After that. My mom is giving me, bread and milk, and cookie and bop, kimchi, soupe so on,

Firstly. I have eaten kimchi stayed on the bop. And that going my mouth. Second, I have soupe that on the spoon,

Excellent delicious!

Passing twenty, I have one bit of bread and one cup of glasses.

Mom! I well have meal!

I rise on the seat, and I am going up my bedroom. I have to sleeping as be tired to me, in the room is yet cozying,

Hi pig? Have good sleeping! I am speaking pig and going in sleeping, after two passing, I am wake up sleeping. Windows still meet the cooling windy. I am feeling cool and worms.

Hi! Pig! Do you have good sleeping? I am questions to pig with smile.

Thanks so!

Pig is question to me with smiling.

What is Today's study and playing?

Mumm...!

Historical study!

Pig is answer to me with smiling.

Prior time, we had learning about that is America historical, pig let me that, pig is smiling to me.

We decide that pig is student, and I am teacher.

Hi! Student! we glade to one more meet time with us.

Sir! pig is rising one hand straight to up,

Could tell me your name? with curious,

Yes! I could you teacher my name! with care,

My name is Nancy!

You know you family my name, but you do not tell me easy.

I do you love and so do you.

Surround is quietly.

Teacher is doing hold chalk on right hand and another hand is doing hold book.

American history is important at world history.

American is starting immigrant's history nations and now first of powerful nations. American is widely than other of normal nations and because of ground is wide, one nation is experience variety clime, also the nation is fully, man have ability and smart, and honest man. And their nation is development than other nations, the man is following the law and love freedom, and important is faith, and they guide freedom and law, and they keep conscience, and each other respect,

Hi! Students! Do you understand that? Nacy is seeing with speaking.

Today is page one hundred five,

I am clapping page and one more seeing pig.

Pig is examining book's page.

Pastime is American's starting and now is American's staying,

Perhaps, they are food' customs and wear has been following them from send me teleconnection Europe's cultural.

They wise that on each other fights, they

could have kept their sprite and culture, and value.

Pig is crazy to the listening speaking to me.

Now, I am teacher to you about historical,

Attention! I am speaking to students and pig.

I am speaking to them stickily.

Go on next page! I am speaking to them.

American is development as science, it is able to human is well-being is able with life that we cannot doing works. Example, at school, hospital, and train, airport, where else we stay in area can be find these.

Once more, I am speaking to them seeing

to,

Go next page,

To now, I am telling you about this page's points.

If you have question, please, give me question!

Hi! Teacher sir?

I am question to you! He has risen his right hand straight to the celling.

Could you tell me about the born rate in American?

That question to me is nice question!

Now, our nation is born rate is low level, its same time is also but American is not concern,

American is receiving the other area 's

immigration. And the problem is resolve but it is causing society problem.

To this problem solve variety nations deep concerning about that, much as American.

Next person? I am steer surrounding slowly.

Surrounding is quietly,

I have closed dark brown color's book with used surface,

``Today is class is ending."

I am folding the book. Other books take on book shelve,

That is geography!

I am smiling to pig,

Teacher? I am tired I have rest to bed, pig is speaking to me and going to sleeping in bedroom.

I am going on study geography. Before I am having study is surround my house's name, now is each nations' city name,

Our nation is name is Seoul and Busan, Ulsan, Desen, kyoung-joo. Marsan... so on.

Each on city. that is Expressionly, and famous,

Example, dammyang in Jolanamdo is famous that bamboo craft. So do I come here that sleepiness.

Student! Today is here till!

 Out of windows is still blowing cooling wind, to my face on the desk downing.

I am one more sleeping oneself. After two hours lately. I am wake up to me by vibration windows by slice windy.

Sky through windows is still blue and clearly. In the sky set in my mind that want fall in clean. Pig is still smile to me,

I want drinking the water and I am getting up the chair and going to the kitchen, mom is watching the tv and I am quietly walks through aisle, reached the on there, I am pick up cup and pure in, and drinking water,

That is very cooling, I crying to the mom,

Could you allow me to go outside?

Mom understands it nearly, she has allowed to me get out to play,

I am going to the out to playing,

I am hold on horn on right hand, over

there come here slice wind is my mind do be clearly, surround is pets' singing their story sent to me rhythm, as soon as walking on the side rode, listen to me please, each other differently, the rhythm is one is high, others is low.

get in my horn in my pocket. twenty-minute walking then in the sky was flying birds with white color, and that side with black color. They sent sounds each other of responsible the sounds.

I was ever seeing the that I am reaching, at there I am picking and take out horns in my pocket.

one is having long leg is sending shot sounds to other.

I am resuming playing my favorite song,
the sounds harmony with cooling windy
go into my ears with vibration.
Its song is mom! Elder sister!
The sound's contents are under line likely.
Mom! elder sister!
Could we live river side,
At yard is brighten gold sand right.
At back door yard is brown leaf's singing
Mom! elder sister!
Could we live liver side.
With song singings I am happy.
My side is over there is narrow water road
is still currency clean and cooling water
currency, I am dipping my both leg in the
water. Water's sound and my mind are

mixed and made to me happily. In the water is small fish, which is up and down moving, sometime be touch my leg, then I am surprised and funny. my head dipping in the water slowly, and rise head in the water, then I see in the water small stone and send, and small fishes.

Long away toward to me listening little sounds is bird's sound and water current sound harmonized, me coming on.

I am wetting my leg do brush by my handkerchief.

I take shoes and walk through the side narrow water line,

By shine is side rode is very worm.

As soon as from one step to two step, I

am feeling very worms.

I am thinking that be back home.

And going back to my house, I am thinking today is very well outside walking to the that, and I am hold the horn that my aunt gives me.

My on walk is light on me because slice windy cooling my face vibration my hair and wear. On going I am thanking, walking on, my mom is wait for me is happy, sometime wind come to me. Surrounds narrow road is nearly grown seeds and do not seed, and do not name flowers, I am my hands reaching to the flower and cutting by my fingers, once small the flower's stream. Get in my noses sweetly smell. they left small dew I had cutting that. I am chewing the flowers' streams.

I am going up narrow road with ugly stones are flat or not Sometime.

Blowing to me with dusty and clean windy mixed.

My walk is satisfied with my conditions is normal forms,

As narrow road passing soon as I am seeing one group's carts come on my front, and bypass to me. The groups have dusty on the contact with dry road rise dusty. Wagon ride on in the cart is to be likely handsome, I am going down road and

Walk for long. Almost reach my house.

Mom! Mom!

I am here right now! I am very delight. Such as I maybe five years passing, such as meeting my mom as likely be feeling.

My mom is still knitting and taking two dogs is sleeping nearly by mom's chair.

Mom! I am going in!

Yes! Could you have wash! Dear?

Mom I am understanding it, I will go now! Prior before I am going entrance door, I am brushing my wears, and directly go to the bathroom. At there I wash hand and head, face, and rubbed my towel,

Mom seems to me and speaking,

Nacy! where are you going?

Mom! I am going outside, the place is narrow water, and narrow rode, at there I am playing horn by the narrow road.
I am pleased that playing with that.
My mom is stopping her work and go in the kitchen,

13. have oneself you want works.

Mom! What's kind of cooking?

Yes! It is bop and kimchi and meat soup with vegetable.

How do you think that?

It is delicious!

On the chair is me, my mother is cooking busily after moment, mom is set on the table meal.

Have a good meal! Mom!

And I am quietly eating the set on meal on the desk.

Outside is more than more slice darkness by the rainy, but in the house is still cozy, on the meal my mom is playing radio.

And listen to song from that's speaker.

I am please, that is involving in my ears.

I am choice that and this, I am choice first bop, and second is soup and kimchi, and soup with grinder meat.

My mom is seeing me with going on smiling.

Mom! Have me allow to go out? My eyes are seeing mom's face,

Yes! My daring! But outside is slice chilly. And you have to wear worm clothes.

With my head doing up and down with smile,

After have meal, I am drinking that orange and vegetable mixed, and I am set up chair with thank about give me meal.

I am directly to my bedroom. And change as my slice thick wear, and passing where two dog is sleeping, going out.

Outside is more then more doing darkness, surround is after raining and slice cooling, I am seeing neighborhood moment, there is still rising smoke in the roof's top, I think that may be doing have meal.

Over there, field's end seen dark white, black cloud group hanging on mountain's top. And pure water toward under area, the water currents fast to down, here is still quietly, sometime slice wind come to my face with cooling feeling.

I am walking for long time on the around my house. On the ground is grabble that is on step by my feet softly. The grabble is brightly that by darkness's lighting with cloud's color.

I am walking along with White fence have orderly staying as cycling. That fence is little broken nearly, after moment, once more seeing the mountain's top, still gathering dark color's clouds. But nearly rain, filed is vegetable, all bow to me likely. Because I am feeling chilly, I am hurry back to my house,

Mom! I am going in!

Mom is doing knit.

Nancy! Have someone?

On the desk is worm milk. Does that have?

Thank you, mom!

I am going to the bathroom and wash hair and face and going the kitchen to drinking milk. In than out is more worm and cozy. Often wind is holding windows with hand. The sound is listening disorderly to me.

Mom have move orderly to staying plate on the kitchen table, Listen to radio on the table,

Mom! I love it!

I am point that is I had eaten of meal, jab-Che is delicious to me,

Mom is smiling to me and speaking to me. Have you latter to eat? I will make to you, at next!

Thank you, mom!

I am bowing to my mom, and I am getting up on the chair.

I am brushing my teeth and going up directly in my bedroom be my friend's pig and my lovely books and desk.

Excuse me? I am careful opening my room's door. And speaking to pig.

Hi! Pig! How do you do that now?

I am ok, Nancy!

Could you have playing that? I am requestioning to pig!

How about you store playing? I am speaking to pig.

How about you that?

It is that you are boss, and I am passenger!

Pig is understanding that explain., and

pig's head moves up and down,

Let us start playing that! I am speaking to pig and sit down my chair.

Excuse me? I am speaking quietly to boss.

Boss is wearing white cylindrical hat,

No problem!

I will buy something! could you help me buying that?

I want taste with sweetly that, I am speaking to boss.

 That bread is recommendation to you!

Boss points Yellow with slice brown color's and little, long that, more add opinion,

that is consist of corn and wheat mixed and add honey,

I am thinking little long,

I am point over there,

That is butter and specially have add milk.

The boss is speaking to me kindly.

May be that is very sweetly for me.

Is it other?

Other is set in cheese have fried as butter,

I will have choice that right now.

It is first recommendation to me,

How much is it. That is two. I am quietly to pig.

Per one is three thousand won. Boss's face is change to the full smile.

It is six thousand won. I am giving boss money,

Thank you have with me to introduction buying the bread.

I am gently having bow and leave the store.

Pig and I are very please, thought the sound long away we are having smile with us.

Out of window is listening coming a chilly wind. In my room is still worm. I am sitting on the chair, and I am writing today's works on my daily note, pig is occasion seeing to me gently.

Mom is still knitting in the living room, sitting on the sofa,

Night is dipping to the darkness. night sky is cover with dark does not seeing.

Mom! Good night! My in-mind mutter word alone to me.

May be Start nation, moon nation are over dark clouds. I am counting one, two, three, four, and quietly be sleeping.

Suddenly, as between the windows frame coming sound, that I wake up on bed, windy come side windows is very cool.

I am firstly bowing to pig. Hi! Pig!

Good morning, Nancy!

Have good sleeping? pig?

I am glade good sleeping Nancy!

I am once more contacting my hand doing up and down on my eyes.

I am opening the windows with little violated wind, doing stretching my two arms, and I am going down to the bathroom, and I am wash with grave sofa on the right stand,

Mom is doing cooking in the kitchen, mom's hair is up rolling and tie with pin, mom's noise is going out sound to sing song, I am directly going out my house. Outside is full of brighten by with dark yellow's sun. surround is cover with wetted the downs chilly. I am walk following the little wet rode, with blue color's shoes, next is plant's leaf is little swing to front and back, sometime listen to sound with birds and pet's message to me with my mind from quietly comfortable.

Neighborhood is still smoking on the little dusty white color's roof.

After passing thirty minutes, I am going

back my house,

Mom! I am going in! I am speaking my mom stay in the kitchen having cooking.

Nacy? Could you wash hand, my mom is question to me as please.

I am washing hand, and I am going in the kitchen, and sit on the chair.

Mom! What's today is menu?

It is bread with blueberry jam, and milk, mom is smiling to me with doing set on the table.

Maybe, that is excellent!

Mom is server to me the meals.

On the desk plate tablecloth with basic red spotted blue color. On which is breads and one of glasses milk.

I am quietly eating that.

Also, my mom is do that. Currency few moments.

Mom is question me about you will doing work today.

I will be study and playing with music, and playing with neighborhood,

Mom! I have one question about build doghouse!

Aha! that will be next day.

One problem is thinking that stay will be whether in or out.

Could you have question me about that?

I think is that stay in, and that made smally. I am speaking to my mom with sincerely.

Ok! That is right way! Mom is doing smile to me,

Mom is asking to neighborhood to make doghouse in person. Neighborhood have allowed that. Neighborhood give me to make woods. The woods size call for large or little, small to her. And taking three and give me the doghouse. Mom pays him to the service rate to make doghouse. That is small and cozy. The dog is so please, barking to him.

The yesterday covered darkness cloud is pass away. I am leaning the windows seeing outside, windows out seen often to me currency cloud on the sky. Windy is sometime blow to my house.

Through moment in think, I get my horn and going outside quietly.

Mom! Can I go the out?

Yes! You can do that! Mom has fully allowed me,

Out is clean and peaceful,

I am going to before gone there. On going I am seeing the narrow water line along swimming small fish with silver color. Air is fresh and as I am breath is cleanly.

Over there seem to me.

The place is still empty, I am sitting on the flat rack, and

 playing horn.

Horn playing sound is in the clean weather is the lighting weight' medium level went to the clean air and widespread long away.

After moment stop playing, and in fall in thinking, surround is quietly.

On the flat rock is little wetted to morning's dews because that, I am stand up the seat, I am slowly walk to garden. I am on walking, plants growing toward sky. The sky is that can be hoping and failed my work, but I see through sky, my hoping to my front of the life and daily have feeling about that is come through.

I am one more one, two walk to my aim.

I have reached the place, and the bench sit on,

The garden is slice quietly, sometime

passing people. I am taking out in my pocket one's candy that my mom is give me that,

I am going the center of garden. And walking along with street tree.

I am seeing back, there one person is coming me,

Hi! Before ever I see person in here, now is white color wear clothes,

How do you do? I am receiving with gladly,

Nice meet you!

Where are you going?

I am going my house! the man is having joking.

I am question him to the meal, he is answer as 'have meal,'

I am bowing to him, and I am back home,
On back home is slice worm, and I go to
nearly narrow water line, there is variety
fishes and plants, ma leg is dipping in the
water, little comfortable to me, there I am
washing hand and face, and have dry with
hand scarf.

I am once more take out horn in my
pocket. And wash my horn dipping in the
water, and wash the horn, that cycling
around under head to dry, that dew down
disappear with wind sounds.

I am sitting up the seat with fate ground
spot and walk to my house.

Then I nearly reached my house, seeing
my mom is that wear hang on lines to dry

wears.

Mom? I am on here!

Mom is seeing into me. Mom's face is changing smile with please,

Nancy! Please! Help me to this works?

Yes! Mom! How can I help for you?

This wear hanging then you have to pick up wears in basket and send to me that!

Ok! Mom! I am little fast walk to the mom, and I am helping my mom works.

There are many wears with yellow, blue, white, red go on.

We orderly set on the line and go in the house,

Mom is going the bathroom and stay that in the corner.

Mom is going kitchen, boil the water to drinking tea and desert with strawberry reservation to me.

I am eating have dip in sugar, and mom is drinking tea.

Nancy! how do you have funny?

All about is normal!

Mom? How do you do work?

I am reading is newspaper, and there are funny stories.

The contents that are collecting money to buy the house.

But he is from younger than me collected money, it means how long taking time, my mom has explained me herself have read story, and I listening the story.

14. if you have to work, that have to work.

Before noon's shiny is little more worm and I my room fold books and going bathroom. In a wash basin, purring water, and my face dipping in the water, I am feeling cooling on my face, and one more go in my room, and my window little opening,
I am involving the book. The book is many contents, may be almost we do not know that.
I moment see pig is smiling to me. And sit up chair and go to the basic stair, there is mom is reading the books. I quietly go in the kitchen, and I have worm one class of

mike, and go out my house,

Outside is raining as little, and I go in the house take umbrella and out, my left-hand hold umbrella and other hand grabs the horn, I am going on the road I see back up my room's windows is about half opened, I am going back my house, and going my room, and have close windows one more is go out.

Then one more seeing back my room's windows, small and cozy seen to me. I am now to be raining with do not playing. Today is that playing   neighborhood' friend have to cancel, I go to the warehouse, but there is little dark, to playing my instrument is normal,

in the warehouse' on well is little broken,
which come on me slice wet winds, to the
other side do so, but little chilly than out,
I am playing instrument, the song's name
is do, re, me song.
This is story is under appearing.
Do, a deer, a female deer.
Re, a drop golden sun.
Me, a name I call myself.
Fa(far), a long longs way to run.
Sol, a needle pulling thread.
La, note to follow so.
Ti, a drink with jam and bread...
Next song is that is playing song is
Arirang!
I am only staying here alone, and alone

speaking singing by horn.

In the warehouse coming and outing with slice cooling windy is passing me being sitting inside corner.

I was pick up candy in the living room setting on table and my pocket I take out that and going in my mouth, in my mouth is fully sweetly.

Firstly, that has eaten and third has eaten and last has eaten on. I am thinking that I will be painting here likely at places, I get up after resting, and quietly opening the door. I was seeing clean sky with blue and white colors with dew of rain. I am going out from warehouse, and I am walking out to the back yard, there is plants growing largely, corn, vegetable, flower is doing brightly.

There is sweetly smell and feeling from plant's leaf with dark green color and flower have combination has mixed by rain.

One's leaf torched lightly my hand, and I am feeling slice cooling with clean,

I thank to if I am being older more than more, I have to school. But do not time get in the school. Yet remain two years to the school.

My mom speaker to me before going to the school, you have to knowledge about study classes. and I have been studying at my room,

I am stopping moment and seeing sky. That is now than before is highly more than, that is cleaning. I am doing head into the down, there is small ant is going walk picking separations hardly.

My mom is doing knitted my wear to reserve this winter, I am going to my room. There is still my friend pig on the desk,

Hello! Pig? I am doing my hand rise up and swing left and right,

Also, pig tell me that how do you playing outside?

Nice a good playing pig! I am speaking to pig doing with smiling.

I am moment siting on the desk. And seeing out through half opened the windows. Outside is listening sounding about birds each other communication. The sounds are clean and natural been to me friendly.

I get up on the chair, and toward to bed, the bed has softly and cozy to me because I like my bed, I am laying on the bed and fall in sleeping about two hours, the sleeping is as much as heaven,

After I am wake up, I am going the kitchen, there is small port, I am pure that my classes, and I am drinking the classes.

My in body is fulling cooling that I am feeling. My mom is reading the book,

Mom! Am I out now? I am speaking with gently to my mom.

That is all-right Nancy!

I was going out alone then dogs were each other playing on

Out is wetted ground go out and more than hotter than early morning by sun shines,

I have turned my sight to the neighborhood. There is man that is Judy's father.

I am going to Judy's father house nearby.

Hi father?

He is turning head to see me,

Hi! Nancy!

How doing here? Judy's father's face is likely seeing before right as working hardly.

Could you tell me? Where is he? I want to

meet Judy!

I am please asking to him.

He is staying in the house! His father is speaking to me with smiling.

Could you have seeing going in now? His father is please asking to me.

Yes! Thank you very much for answer me.

I am speaking with us, and I am going in Judy's house, Judy's in house is larger than my house and widely. Specially on the basic can see the two floors,

I am carefully calling for Judy. Then he is answer for me about I am calling for on.

Judy! how do you do?

Nice a meet you! Nancy?

How do you do that? I am question to

him with gently.

He has responsible my questions with smile in more than more face to me.

I love it. How place the playing inside or outside?

We are going out Judy's house and that shaded the house by hot shiny, Judy and I have played that noun is song name's firstly noun connection with that is calling that my speaking alphabet,

Example if I will firstly colling for sound of music is do re me song, and firstly noun!

You answer is has to answer start noun song as `do.'

Judy and I have playing with, and I am going to my house. I am on going take out my horn, have plying.

In the sky still hotting on my breath by sunshine,

Mom! I am getting in now!

Mom is cooking in the kitchen, slice question me,

how do you get there?

Yes! Interesting and well done!

Then kitchen windows by left come sounds by bird's singing.

My view toward windows, moment birds shortly stay on and flying to the long away to me in the house.

Hi! My cute little baby! Could you send me the napkin?

Yes! Mom! I am picking up that on the

desk is it and my mom giving that.

Thank your give me, my cute little baby!

Mom is busily making food cooking.

Mom! I am asking please to her.

Why? Mom is answer that.

Today work is near half complete that.

What's works? Mom is question me.

Neighborhood with playing and studying!

Nacy! congratulations that.

Mom is meal set on the table. And sitting on the chair front me.

Mom? what is today menu?

Today menu is fried fish. Could you have delicious meal.

Mom and I have meal quietly. The meal is very forming for me.

I am brash my teeth and washing hand
and I am going up stair being my world.
My room is cozy and sweetly. I am in.
always pig greet to me.
Hi! pig!
Could are asking me you have problem? I
am please question to pig.
Pig is smiling to me,
Today study is what 's class?
Today class is mathematics!
how long the class that we must study to
that?
You are learning that we had study that
class. The contents are plus, miners, and
share, multiplication.
Today is multiplication. Pig is speaking to

me with each side shoulder powerful rising.

Hi! Nacy! I am quizzing to you about multiplication.

Firstly, is you answer, two multiplication four?

It is twelve! I am responsible about the question Fastly.

Next is thirty multiplication two?

So do I responsible that is sixty.

Pig and I am playing with please. Each other talking with us that game.

Little passing on noon. I am shortly sleeping on the desk. Over there is coming still slice cooling wind from the basically white, blue's sky.

White color with curtain Hanging on the front Windows's tip is being vibration by windy with worm shiny.

I have folded my book, and I am going kitchen and have drinking juice making orange. Mom is still quietly knitting.

I am going out to find place with chilly. My pocket's left is fully candy and right is horn, I have found place with normal: do not hot stage and do not' chilly stage.

Nearly is newspaper, which placed on the ground and angle side set on small stones. I am lay on the that, I am feeling comfortable. My arms are under my head, I see the sky with please. In the sky is still bule. and sometime currency white clouds on the blue basic slowly.

I take out one's candy and to my mouth going in. my mouth is full as sweetly, in the sky dropping dew is my face nearly feeling. In the house listen to barking by dogs.

Near flower is slice vibration by slice windy. My head turn to the neighborhood, there still horse is eating seeds with his young, the Youngs are playing with running each other.

I do rise the body place, and hurry going to my room, on the bookshelf that take out my ant lend me that, lightly geography book. I am taking on that, going the place and laying on the newspaper. and reading the book, the book is interesting with me. After Passing one hour, sky is yet hot.

I am folding book and have order my place. I am glancing my room, there is brightly by sunshine. I am walking to my house there is mom is study with book, Mom! could help me this book's study.? Mom is toward to me. And speaking to.

Cut what problem is it?

I am reading this book, but I do not read this book.

It is difficulty a noun, I am speaking to her. Maybe you have to basic book, and your level do not match.

I will teacher you every day, firstly. I will be

choice as easy level book.

Tomorrow. I will be purchasing the basically book at bookstore.

The book will be ease for you!

Yes! Mom! I will learn basic levels that mom tall me a way.

Thank you, mom!

I am bowing my mom, and I am going on my room, on back call me,

Could you have desert?

I am ok! my mom!

I am listening to mom's speaking to me. And going to the kitchen. on the desk was juice and bread, after I am all some. I am going my bedroom and sleeping in my dream.

After rolling doughnuts in grounds to be playing

발   행 | 2024 년 5 월 9 일
저   자 | 김용호
펴낸이 | 한건희
펴낸곳 | 주식회사 부크크
출판사등록 | 2014.07.15.(제 2014-16 호)
주   소 | 서울특별시 금천구 가산디지털 1 로 119 SK 트윈타워 A 동 305 호
전   화 | 1670-8316
이메일 | info@bookk.co.kr

ISBN | 979-11-410-8454-7
www.bookk.co.kr
ⓒ 김용호 2024